weightwatchers

Master
Your

Meals
and Snacks

Weight Watchers Publishing Group

VP, Editorial Director **Nancy Gagliardi**
Creative Director **Ed Melnitsky**
Photo Director **Deborah Hardt**
Managing Editor **Diane Pavia**
Assistant Edito**r Katerina Gkionis**
Food Editor **Eileen Runyan**
Editor **Deborah Mintcheff**
Production Manager **Alan Biederman**
Photographers **Antonis Achilleos, Iain Bagwell, Ryan Dausch,**
Philip Friedman, Dana Gallagher, Frances Janisch, John Kernick,
David Malosh, Kate Mathis, Hector Sanchez, Ann Stratton,
Romulo Yanes,
Art Director **Liz Trovato**

Front Cover: Chicken and Corn Salad, page 60

About Weight Watchers

Weight Watchers International, Inc. is the world's leading provider of weight-management services, operating globally through a network of company-owned and franchise operations. Weight Watchers holds nearly 45,000 meetings each week worldwide, at which members receive group support and education about healthful eating patterns, behavior modification, and physical activity. Weight-loss and weight-management results vary by individual. We recommend that you attend Weight Watchers meetings to benefit from the supportive environment and follow the comprehensive Weight Watchers program, which includes a food plan, an activity plan, and a behavioral component.

WeightWatchers.com provides subscription weight-management products, such as eTools and Weight Watchers Mobile, and is the leading internet-based weight-management provider in the world. In addition, Weight Watchers offers a wide range of products, publications (including **Weight Watchers Magazine**, which is available on newsstands and in Weight Watchers meeting rooms), and programs for people interested in weight loss and control. For the Weight Watchers meeting nearest you, call **1-800-651-6000**. For information about bringing Weight Watchers to your workplace, call **1-800-8AT-WORK**.

Shrimp Risotto with Snap Peas p70

Contents

About Our Recipes

While losing weight isn't only about what you eat, Weight Watchers realizes the critical role it plays in your success and overall good health. That's why our philosophy is to offer great-tasting, easy recipes that are nutritious as well as delicious. We make every attempt to use wholesome ingredients and to ensure that our recipes fall within the recommendations of the U.S. Dietary Guidelines for Americans for a diet that promotes health and reduces the risk for disease. If you have special dietary needs, consult with your health-care professional for advice on a diet that is best for you, then adapt these recipes to meet your specific nutritional needs.

To achieve these good-health goals and get the maximum satisfaction from the foods you eat, we suggest you keep the following information in mind while preparing our recipes:

Getting Started, Keeping Going, and Good Nutrition

- Recipes in this book have been developed for Weight Watchers members who are just getting started (with Simple Start), and for members who are further along toward their goals, including those who are using our *PointsPlus*® plan.

- *PointsPlus* values are given for each recipe. They're assigned based on the amount of protein, carbohydrates, fat, and fiber contained in a single serving of a recipe.

- *PointsPlus* values have been calculated using Recipe Builder at **WeightWatchers.com**.

- Substitutions made to the ingredients will alter the per-serving nutritional information and may affect the *PointsPlus* value.

- Our recipes meet Weight Watchers Good Health Guidelines for eating lean proteins and fiber-rich whole grains and for having at least five servings of vegetables and fruits and two servings of low-fat or fat-free dairy products a day, while limiting your intake of saturated fat, sugar, and sodium.

- Health agencies recommend limiting sodium intake. To stay in line with this recommendation, we keep sodium levels in our recipes reasonably low; to boost flavor, we often include fresh herbs or a squeeze of citrus instead of salt. If you don't have to restrict your sodium, feel free to add a touch more salt as desired.

- In the recipes, a green triangle (▲) or an ingredient marked in **green** indicates Weight Watchers® Power Foods.

- **To make it a meal** suggestions have a *PointsPlus* value of **0** unless otherwise stated.

- Recipes that work with Simple Start are listed on page xii. Find more details about Simple Start at your meeting.

- For information about the science behind lasting weight loss and more, please visit **WeightWatchers.com/science.**

Calculations Not What You Expected?

You might expect some of the **PointsPlus** values in this book to be lower when some of the foods they're made from, such as fruits and vegetables, have no **PointsPlus** values. Most fruits and veggies have no **PointsPlus** values when served as a snack or part of a meal, like a cup of berries with a sandwich. But if these foods are part of a recipe, their fiber and nutrient content are incorporated into the recipe calculations. These nutrients can affect the **PointsPlus** value.

Shopping For Ingredients

As you learn to eat healthier and add more Weight Watchers Power Foods to your meals, remember these tips for choosing foods wisely:

Lean Meats and Poultry Purchase lean meats and poultry, and trim them of all visible fat before cooking. When poultry is cooked with the skin on, we recommend removing the skin before eating. Nutritional information for recipes that include meat, poultry, and fish is based on cooked, skinless boneless portions (unless otherwise stated), with the fat trimmed.

Seafood Whenever possible, our recipes call for seafood that is sustainable and deemed the most healthful for human consumption so that your choice of seafood is not only good for the oceans but also good for you. For more information about the best seafood choices and to download a pocket guide, go to **environmentaldefensefund.org** or **montereybayaquarium.org.** For information about mercury and seafood go to **weightwatchers.com.**

Produce For best flavor, maximum nutrient content, and the lowest prices, buy fresh local produce, such as vegetables, leafy greens, and fruits, in season. Rinse them thoroughly before using, and keep a supply of cut-up vegetables and fruits in your refrigerator for convenient healthy snacks.

Whole Grains Explore your market for whole-grain products, such as whole wheat and whole-grain breads and pastas, brown rice, bulgur, barley, cornmeal, whole wheat couscous, oats, and quinoa, to enjoy with your meals.

Read the Recipe Take a couple of minutes to read through the ingredients and directions before you start to prepare a recipe. This will prevent you from discovering midway through that you don't have an important ingredient or that a recipe requires several hours of marinating. And it's also a good idea to assemble all ingredients and utensils within easy reach before you begin a recipe.

Weighing and Measuring The success of any recipe depends on accurate weighing and measuring. The effectiveness of the Weight Watchers Program and the accuracy of the nutritional analysis depend on correct measuring as well. Use the following techniques:

- Weigh foods such as meat, poultry, and fish on a food scale.

- To measure liquids, use a standard glass or plastic measuring cup placed on a level surface. For amounts less than ¼ cup, use standard measuring spoons.

- To measure dry ingredients, use metal or plastic measuring cups that come in ¼-, ⅓-, ½-, and 1-cup sizes. Fill the appropriate cup, and level it with the flat edge of a knife or spatula. For amounts less than ¼ cup, use standard measuring spoons.

Introduction

Weight Watchers is with you—and for you—all the way to your weight goal. Our meetings provide support, motivation, and accountability. Our digital tools—the tools on **WeightWatchers.com** and a robust suite of apps for smartphones and iPad—provide our biggest database of foods and their ***PointsPlus*** values; a barcode scanner; great community features; thousands of recipes and articles; and more. These products are designed to help you toward your goal.

Our newest plan is Simple Start. It will get you off to a great beginning. See page xii for a list of recipes, built from good-for-you foods that work with Simple Start so you can create two weeks of meals. From there, either keep going with our Simply Filling technique (which is what Simple Start is based on), or try our flexible ***PointsPlus*** system.

How to Use This Book

We've set up the recipes in each chapter according to how much time it will take to prepare them—no time, in a little time, or in more time.

Fix It These recipes are really simple and serve one. They require either no cooking or a microwave or toaster oven for quick heating or cooking and are ideal when you have no time to spare.

Make It These recipes may require using a pot or pan for some easy cooking. They also serve one and are your go-to dishes when you have a few extra minutes.

Cook It These recipes are real standouts. Enjoy them when you aren't in a hurry to get breakfast, lunch, dinner—or dessert—on the table or have some weekend time to spend in the kitchen. They serve four or more.

Want to make it a complete meal? We've provided lots of smart, healthful ways to turn our tempting dishes into complete meals in our To Make It a Meal tips that follow many of the recipes. Success has never been this simple—or delicious!

Make Power Foods as tasty as they are good for you with proper cooking. Be sure to check out our Steaming Savvy, page xiv on how to steam vegetables, as well as our Great Grains, page xv on choosing and cooking whole grains.

Simple Start Pantry Essentials

Simplicity is key to getting started. Set up the Simple Start Pantry Essentials we've created here. Simple Start is built from Power Foods. Here are all the Weight Watchers® Power Foods you'll come across in the recipes in this book. The ingredients are easy to find in your local supermarket. And to make it easy on yourself, for your first two weeks, check out our recipes that work with Simple Start, listed on page xii.

On the Shelf

Applesauce (unsweetened)

Beans (canned, dried)

Bread (light, reduced-calorie)

Broth (beef, chicken, vegetable)

Clams (baby)

Corn (kernels, cream-style)

Onions & potatoes

Pasta & noodles (whole wheat pasta, brown rice stick noodles)

Pimiento & roasted peppers (not oil-packed)

Pumpkin puree (canned)

Rice (brown)

Split peas (dried yellow)

Tomato sauce (canned)

Tomatoes (peeled whole, diced, petite diced, crushed, stewed, without added fat or sugar)

Whole grains (quick-cooking barley, bulgur, whole wheat couscous, old-fashioned oats, plain popcorn, quinoa)

In the Fridge

Cheese (fat-free Cheddar, cream cheese, feta, mozzarella, ricotta, Swiss)

Crabmeat (canned)

Eggs & fat-free egg substitute

Fresh fruits & vegetables (various)

Half-and-half (fat-free)

Milk (fat-free regular, fat-free plain soy, vanilla soy)

Polenta (fat-free in a tube)

Salsa (fat-free tomato & salsa verde)

Sour cream (fat-free)

Sun-dried tomatoes (not oil-packed)

Tofu (silken, reduced-fat firm, regular firm)

Yogurt (plain fat-free Greek, plain fat-free regular, light vanilla fat-free)

In the Freezer

Broccoli (stir-fry mix, chopped)

Corn kernels

Fruit (unsweetened blueberries, cherries, mixed fruit)

Green bell pepper (chopped)

Meatless soy crumbles

Onion (chopped and small white)

Peas (baby and regular)

Shelled edamame

Easy ways to add exotic flavor

- Squeezable tomato and basil pestos
- Tarragon mustard
- Orange flower water
- Lemon, garlic, and rosemary-flavored olive oils
- Anchovy paste
- Smoked salt
- Cholula hot pepper sauce
- Balsamic vinegar glaze
- Preserved lemons
- White truffle oil

Recipes That Work with Simple Start

For your first two weeks, pick only from our best-for-weight-loss meals and snacks below that work with Simple Start. Mix and match the recipes any way you like each day.

More quick snacks that follow Simple Start

- ½ apple and 1 ounce fat-free Cheddar cheese for **2 PointsPlus** value

- 3 cups light microwave-popped popcorn for **2 PointsPlus** value

- ½ cup plain fat-free yogurt with ½ cup berries for **3 PointsPlus** value

- ½ cup fat-free cottage cheese with 3 carrot sticks and 3 celery sticks for **2 PointsPlus** value

- 1 slice of reduced-calorie bread topped with 1 ounce sliced cooked turkey breast and ¼ cup roasted red pepper (water packed) for **3 PointsPlus** value

Steaming Savvy

Simplicity itself, steaming is a cooking method where the food is cooked over boiling water in a covered pot on the stovetop or in a microwavable dish in the microwave. There are several benefits to steaming vegetables. It enables them to retain their nutrients since they sit over—not in—water, and steaming helps vegetables to keep their vibrant color and cook just until crisp-tender—not waterlogged and limp. To ensure vegetables are cooked in the same amount of time, leave them whole or cut into uniform-size pieces, preferably on the smaller side. Keep in mind that the larger the pieces of food, the longer the cooking time.

How to Steam Vegetables on the Stovetop

Unlike steaming in a microwave, the length of time it takes to steam on the stovetop is not affected by the amount of vegetables. Add about ½ inch water to a saucepan or skillet and insert a steamer basket. Cover and bring to a boil. Add the vegetable, cover the pot tightly, and steam until tender. Refer to the chart for approximate cooking times.

How to Steam Vegetables in a Microwave

Add about 2 tablespoons water to a microwavable bowl or casserole. Add the vegetables and cover the dish with a piece of microwavable plastic wrap venting one corner, a sheet of wax paper, or microwavable cover. If using Weight Watchers microwavable container, place the food on the rack, snap the lid closed, and lift the colored vent tab. Microwave on High until the vegetables are tender, following the guidelines in the chart. Keep in mind that the cooking time will vary depending on the wattage of the microwave.

Vegetable Cooking Chart

This chart is based on an 800-watt microwave.

Food	One Serving	Approximate Microwave Cooking Time	Approximate Stovetop Cooking Time
Regular asparagus, trimmed	3 ounces	1 ½ minutes	6 minutes
Broccoli florets	3 ounces	1 ½ minutes	5 minutes
Sliced carrot	3 ounces	1 ½ minutes	4 minutes
Corn kernels	3 ounces	1 ½ minutes	4 minutes
Green beans	3 ounces	1 ½ minutes	6 minutes
Green peas	3 ounces	1 minute	4 minutes
Potatoes, baby	2 (1 ½-ounce)	3 ½ minutes	10 minutes
Potatoes, whole	1 (4-ounce)	3 ½ minutes	12 minutes

Great Grains

When it comes to choosing what to eat, whole grains are the way to go. They are a great source of antioxidants and fiber, which may help lower cholesterol.

What is a Whole Grain?

A whole grain contains all its essential parts: the bran (outer covering), the endosperm (large inner part), and the germ (nutrient-rich heart). For grain to be "whole," 100% of the bran, endosperm, and germ must be intact. That is why it is the healthiest choice that you can make.

What to Choose

Look for these whole grain products in your supermarket, health-food store, or big box store:

Whole Wheat: bulgur, couscous, farro, kamut, spelt, and wheat berries

Whole Grain Rice: brown rice, Bhutanese rice, and wild rice

Whole Corn: cornmeal, grits, hominy, and plain air-popped popcorn

Also: amaranth, barley, buckwheat, millet, quinoa, rye, spelt, whole grain pasta, and brown udon noodles

Stamp of Approval

To be sure you are buying a 100% whole grain, look for the Whole Grain Council's rectangular yellow stamp on the package. Or check for these key words on the label: whole grain, whole wheat, whole, and stoneground.

Now that you know how excellent whole grains are for you, here's all you need to know to prepare them. The key is to cook them just until tender and flavorful, not soft and mushy. By cooking whole grains in the right amount of water, they retain all their vitamins and nutrients. Use the chart on page xvi. Your body will thank you.

Whole Grains Cooking Chart

Amount of Grain (1 cup)	Add Water or Broth	Bring to Boil Then Simmer	Approximate Yield
Amaranth	6 cups	15 to 20 minutes	2 ½ cups
Pearled barley	3 cups	45 to 60 minutes	3 ½ cups
Buckwheat (kasha)	2 cups	15 to 20 minutes	4 cups
Bulgur	2 cups	10 to 12 minutes	3 cups
Farro	2 ½ cups	25 to 40 minutes	3 cups
Kamut	4 cups	soak up to several hours in the 4 cups liquid; cook 45 to 60 minutes	3 cups
Millet (hulled)	2 ½ cups	25 to 35 minutes	4 cups
Oats (steel cut)	4 cups	30 minutes	3 cups
Quinoa	2 cups	12 to 15 minutes	3 cups
Rice, brown	2 ½ cups	25 to 45 minutes	3 cups
Rice, wild	3 cups	45 to 55 minutes	3½ cups
Spelt	4 cups	soak up to several hours in the 4 cups liquid; cook 45 to 60 minutes	3 cups
Wheat berries	4 cups	soak up to several hours in the 4 cups liquid; cook 45 to 60 minutes	2 ½ cups

Good to Know

• To cut down on the cooking time, presoak grain in water for up to 6 hours. During this time, it will begin to soften and swell. Cook as directed, adding more water, if needed.

• The cooking times for grains vary, depending on how old they are and the type of pot used.

• Cook up a double batch. Stored in an airtight container, cooked grains will keep for up to 4 days in the refrigerator. Use them to create a tasty salad or side dish.

brea

eat
kfast

eggs, cereal, pancakes, and waffles

Multigrain Cereal

A.M. Couscous SERVES 1

Combine ½ **cup fat-free milk** and **pinch ground cinnamon** in small microwavable bowl. Microwave on High just until it boils. Stir in ¼ **cup whole wheat couscous**. Cover and let stand 5 minutes. Fluff couscous with fork. Top with ½ **diced small pear or apple**.

 Per serving (1 cup)

To make it a meal
Include 1 slice of light oatmeal bread, toasted and topped with 1 slice of fat-free American cheese. This will increase the **PointsPlus** value by **2**.

Multigrain Cereal SERVES 1

Mix together **2 tablespoons quick-cooking barley**, **2 table-spoons bulgur**, **2 tablespoons old-fashioned (rolled) oats**, and **⅔ cup water** in 1-quart microwavable bowl. Microwave on High 2 minutes. Stir in **1 tablespoon dark raisins** and **pinch ground cinnamon**; microwave on High 3 minutes. Top with **1 tablespoon chopped almonds**.

 **Per serving (⅔ cup)**

Veggie Cup Scramble SERVES 1

Spray 12-ounce microwavable mug with nonstick spray. Add **1 large egg**, **1 tablespoon fat-free milk**, **¼ cup cut up asparagus**, and **¼ cup quartered small white or cremini mushrooms**; mix well. Microwave on High 30 seconds; stir. Microwave until egg is set, 30–45 seconds longer. Sprinkle with **2 tablespoons crumbled fat-free feta cheese**.

 Per serving (1 cup)

To make it a meal

Serve 2 slices of reduced-calorie bread—any kind you like—alongside this satisfying breakfast dish (2 slices of reduced-calorie bread will increase the *PointsPlus* value by *3*).

PB and Banana Bagel SERVES 1

Preheat toaster oven broiler. Spread **2 teaspoons reduced-fat peanut butter** on **½ small bagel**. Top with **½ sliced small banana** and sprinkle with **¼ teaspoon cinnamon-sugar**. Broil until sugar is browned, 1–2 minutes.

 Per serving (½ topped bagel)

To make it a meal

Finish with a dish of fresh orange and grapefruit sections and get a healthful dose of vitamins and fiber. Your body will thank you.

Veggie Cup Scramble

BLT Waffle Sandwich

BLT Waffle Sandwich   SERVES 1

Preheat toaster oven to 375°F. Spray toaster oven tray with nonstick spray. Place **2 slices Canadian bacon** on tray; bake until heated through, about 2 minutes per side. Toast **2 low-fat frozen whole wheat or multigrain waffles**. Top 1 waffle with **1 cup loosely packed salad greens**, bacon, **2 slices tomato**, and **2 teaspoons fat-free creamy dressing**. Cover with remaining waffle.

 Per serving (1 sandwich)

Pancake Deluxe   SERVES 1

Toast **1 frozen multigrain pancake**. Top with ½ cup sliced banana, ¼ cup fresh raspberries, **1 tablespoon low-calorie pancake syrup**, and **1 ½ teaspoons chopped unsalted pistachios**.

 Per serving (1 pancake and ¾ cup topping)

To make it a meal

Enjoy an 8-ounce fat-free cappuccino sprinkled with cinnamon for **1** additional **PointsPlus** value.

Pepper-Cheese Muffin   SERVES 1

Preheat toaster oven to 375°F. Spray toaster oven tray with nonstick spray. Place **2 slices Canadian bacon** on tray; cook until heated through, about 2 minutes per side. Top ½ **toasted English muffin** with bacon, **¼ cup low-fat cottage cheese**, and ½ **sliced pepperoncini**.

 Per serving (1 topped muffin)

To make it a meal

Start your breakfast off with a refreshing juicy orange, broken into segments.

Peach-Yogurt Parfait   SERVES 1

Alternately layer **¾ cup unsweetened canned sliced peaches**, drained, and **½ cup vanilla fat-free yogurt** in parfait glass. Sprinkle with **2 tablespoons low-fat granola**.

 Per serving (1 ½ cups)

Layered Fruit Smoothie   SERVES 1

Combine **½ chopped small mango**, **⅓ cup lemon fat-free yogurt**, and **1 ice cube** in blender; blend until smooth. Pour into glass. Combine **½ small banana**, **⅓ cup lemon fat-free yogurt**, **⅓ cup fresh raspberries**, and **1 ice cube** in blender; blend until smooth. Pour over mango-yogurt mixture.

 Per serving (2 cups)

To make it a meal

Add sliced fresh strawberries or raspberries to this delicious parfait for bright color and good-for-you antioxidants.

Middle Eastern–Style Breakfast Bagel
SERVES 1

Spread **¼ cup hummus** over **1 split and toasted whole wheat bagel thin**. Top evenly with **½ cup quartered cherry tomatoes**, **2 tablespoons chopped cucumber**, **2 chopped pitted Kalamata olives**, and **1 ½ teaspoons chopped red or white onion**.

 Per serving (1 topped bagel)

Peach-Yogurt Parfait

Tomato Scramble

Tomato Scramble SERVES 1

Heat **½ teaspoon canola oil** in small nonstick skillet set over medium heat. Add **½ chopped tomato** and **1 thinly sliced small shallot**; cook until shallot is softened, about 4 minutes. Transfer to small bowl. Wipe out skillet. Add **½ teaspoon oil** to skillet and set over medium heat. Pour in **⅔ cup fat-free egg substitute** and **2 teaspoons chopped fresh basil**; cook, stirring eggs with heatproof spatula, until softly scrambled, about 2 minutes; transfer to plate. Top with tomato mixture.

 Per serving (1 ¼ cups)

To make it a meal

Start with a wedge of cantaloupe and serve a slice of toasted reduced-calorie bread topped with fat-free cottage cheese alongside the eggs (1 slice of reduced-calorie bread topped with ⅓ cup of fat-free cottage cheese will increase the *PointsPlus* value by **2**).

Goat Cheese and Pimiento Egg Wrap

SERVES 1

Spray small nonstick skillet with nonstick spray and set over medium heat. Pour in **½ cup fat-free egg substitute** and sprinkle with **1 tablespoon crumbled soft goat cheese**. Cook eggs, stirring with heatproof spatula, until softly scrambled, about 2 minutes. Spoon eggs onto **1 (7-inch) fat-free flour tortilla**; sprinkle with **1 tablespoon chopped pimiento** and roll up to enclose filling.

 Per serving (1 wrap)

Shrimp, Bell Pepper, and Thyme Omelette   SERVES 1

Whisk together **1 cup fat-free egg substitute**, **1 teaspoon fresh thyme leaves**, **1 teaspoon snipped fresh chives**, **pinch salt**, and **pinch black pepper** in small bowl. Spray small nonstick skillet with nonstick spray and set over medium heat. Add **¼ chopped red bell pepper** and **1 finely chopped small shallot**; cook, stirring, until bell pepper is softened, about 3 minutes. Stir in **2 ounces cooked small shrimp**; transfer mixture to small bowl. Wipe out skillet. Heat **½ teaspoon canola oil** in skillet over medium heat. Pour in egg mixture and cook, stirring occasionally with heatproof spatula to let uncooked egg flow underneath, just until set, about 6 minutes. Sprinkle bell pepper mixture over half of omelette; fold unfilled half over filling to enclose. Slide omelette onto plate.

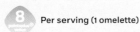 **Per serving (1 omelette)**

To make it a meal

Begin your breakfast with a generous bowl of diced mango, papaya, and sliced strawberries. And consider adding 3 or 4 sliced white or cremini mushrooms to the omelette along with the bell pepper.

Aegean Frittata   SERVES 1

Heat **1 ½ teaspoons olive oil** in small nonstick skillet over medium heat. Add **¼ cup frozen hash brown potatoes**, **2 tablespoons frozen chopped onion**, **2 tablespoons frozen chopped green bell pepper**, **¼ teaspoon dried oregano**, **pinch salt**, and **pinch black pepper**; cook, stirring, until vegetables are tender and golden, about 7 minutes. Meanwhile, beat together **1 large egg** and **1 large egg white** in small bowl. Add eggs to skillet and cook, lifting edges frequently with heatproof spatula to let uncooked egg flow underneath, until eggs are almost set, about 3 minutes. Sprinkle **1 tablespoon crumbled feta cheese** over frittata. Reduce heat to low; cook, covered, until cheese is softened, about 3 minutes. Slide frittata onto plate.

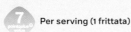 **Per serving (1 frittata)**

**Shrimp, Bell Pepper,
and Thyme Omelette**

Sunnyside Potato and Vegetable Hash

SERVES 1

Heat **½ teaspoon olive oil** in medium nonstick skillet over medium heat. Add **1 cubed cooked small red potato (about 3 ounces)**, **½ chopped small red bell pepper**, **½ finely chopped small onion**, **1 minced garlic clove**, **pinch salt**, and **pinch black pepper**. Cover and cook, stirring occasionally, until vegetables are lightly browned, about 6 minutes. Stir in **½ teaspoon dried sage**. Transfer potato mixture to plate; keep warm. Wipe out skillet. Spray skillet with nonstick spray and set over medium heat. Break **1 large egg** into skillet; cover and cook until white is set and yolk is still soft, 2–3 minutes. Place egg on top of hash.

To make it a meal

Make this a special weekend dish by cooking two large eggs instead of one. This will increase the **PointsPlus** value by **2**.

 Per serving (about 1 cup hash browns with 1 egg)

Savory Baked Egg   SERVES 1

Preheat toaster oven to 400°F. Lightly oil ½-cup ramekin. Crack **1 large egg** into ramekin. Add **1 tablespoon canned tomato sauce with onions, green peppers, and celery**, **1 tablespoon crumbled fat-free feta cheese**, and **1 tablespoon snipped fresh chives**. Bake until white of egg is set and yolk is still soft, 8–10 minutes. Serve with **1 slice toasted reduced-calorie whole wheat bread**.

 Per serving (1 garnished egg and 1 slice toast)

Zucchini-Cheese "Pancake" SERVES 1

Mix together ½ cup fat-free egg substitute, ½ cup shredded zucchini, ½ slice reduced-calorie whole wheat bread made into crumbs, 2 tablespoons shredded fat-free Cheddar cheese, and ½ teaspoon dried oregano or basil in medium bowl. Spray small nonstick skillet with nonstick spray and set over medium heat. Add egg mixture and cook, without stirring, until egg is set, about 3 minutes per side.

 Per serving (1 pancake)

To make it a meal

Start with half of a ruby (or other variety) red grapefruit and end with a latte. An 8-ounce latte made with fat-free milk will increase the *PointsPlus* value by 2.

Polenta Hot Cakes SERVES 1

Cut ¼ pound prepared fat-free polenta (from 18-ounce tube) into 4 rounds. Heat **1 teaspoon olive oil** in small skillet over medium heat. Add polenta and cook until lightly browned, about 3 minutes per side. Transfer to plate. Spoon **⅓ cup unsweetened applesauce** on top of polenta and drizzle with **1 ½ teaspoons raspberry syrup**.

 Per serving (4 topped polenta rounds)

Cinnamon-Apple Oatmeal   SERVES 1

Bring **½ cup water** and **pinch salt** to boil in small saucepan.
Stir in **½ cup old-fashioned (rolled) oats**. Reduce heat
to simmer and cook, stirring, until oats are softened and
liquid is absorbed, about 5 minutes. Remove from heat; stir
in **½ diced unpeeled red apple**, **¼ teaspoon ground
cinnamon**, and **pinch ground nutmeg**. Cover and let stand
3 minutes. Serve topped with **½ cup plain fat-free soy milk**.

 Per serving (1 cup)

Berry Quinoa   SERVES 1

Combine **½ cup unsweetened almond milk** and **¼ cup
quinoa** in small saucepan and bring to boil. Reduce heat;
cover and simmer until quinoa is tender and liquid is
absorbed, about 15 minutes. Remove from heat and let stand
5 minutes. Stir in **½ cup mixed fresh berries** and **pinch
ground cinnamon**. Spoon quinoa mixture into bowl; top with
1 tablespoon blueberry syrup.

 Per serving (1 ¼ cups)

To make it a meal

Add an additional
¼ cup berries to this
special breakfast
bowl, then end the
meal by sipping a
chai tea latte. An
8-ounce chai tea latte
made with fat-free
milk will increase the
PointsPlus value by **2**.

Berry Quinoa

Eggs, Lox, and Onions with Chopped Salad SERVES 4

2 tablespoons extra-virgin olive oil

Juice of ½ lemon

¼ plus ⅛ teaspoon black pepper

⅛ teaspoon salt

▲ 1 cucumber, diced

▲ 1 large tomato, diced

▲ 1 orange or red bell pepper, diced

1 teaspoon unsalted butter

▲ 2 onions, chopped

▲ 2 large eggs

▲ 5 large egg whites

▲ 3 tablespoons fat-free milk

¼ pound lox or smoked salmon, chopped

▲ ¼ cup fat-free sour cream

1 tablespoon snipped fresh chives

To make it a meal

Serve a basket of crisply toasted light English muffins alongside this classic New York Sunday morning dish (1 light English muffin per serving will increase the **PointsPlus** value by **3**).

1 To make salad, whisk together oil, lemon juice, ⅛ teaspoon of black pepper, and the salt in medium bowl. Add cucumber, tomato, and bell pepper; toss until mixed well.

2 To make eggs, melt butter in large nonstick skillet over medium-low heat. Add onions and cook, stirring, until softened, about 8 minutes.

3 Meanwhile, whisk together eggs, egg whites, and milk in medium bowl until frothy. Increase heat to medium; pour egg mixture over onions. Swirl to cover bottom of pan; cook about 15 seconds (do not stir). Add lox and remaining ¼ teaspoon black pepper; cook, stirring, until eggs are set, about 3 minutes longer. Divide eggs evenly among 4 plates; top with sour cream and chives. Serve with salad.

 Per serving (about ⅔ cup egg mixture with 1 tablespoon sour cream and about 1 cup salad)

Silver Dollar Pancakes with Chocolate Chips   SERVES 6

1 cup all-purpose flour

½ cup white whole wheat flour

2 teaspoons baking powder

¼ teaspoon salt

1 cup low-fat (1%) milk

▲ 1 large egg, separated

1 tablespoon unsalted butter, melted

½ teaspoon vanilla extract

▲ 1 large egg white

3 tablespoons sugar

4 tablespoons strawberry syrup

2 tablespoons mini semisweet chocolate chips

1 Whisk together all-purpose flour, white whole wheat flour, baking powder, and salt in medium bowl. Whisk together milk, egg yolk, butter, and vanilla in small bowl. Pour milk mixture over flour mixture; stir just until combined.

2 With electric mixer on medium-high speed, beat 2 egg whites in medium bowl until soft peaks form when beaters are lifted. Gradually add sugar, 1 tablespoon at a time, beating until stiff peaks form when beaters are lifted. With rubber spatula, gently fold half of beaten egg whites into flour mixture; fold in remaining whites just until no white streaks remain.

3 Spray nonstick griddle or 12-inch skillet with nonstick spray and set over medium heat. Drop heaping tablespoonfuls of batter onto griddle, about 2 inches apart. Cook until bubbles appear and edges of pancakes look dry, 2–3 minutes. Turn pancakes and cook until golden on second side, about 2 minutes longer. Transfer to platter; keep warm. Repeat with remaining batter, spraying griddle with nonstick spray between batches, making total of 30 pancakes.

4 To make topping, mix together strawberry syrup and chocolate chips in small bowl. Serve with pancakes.

 Per serving (5 pancakes with 1 tablespoon topping)

Baked French Toast

Baked French Toast SERVES 6

- ▲ 12 slices reduced-calorie whole wheat bread
- 2 cups low-fat (1%) milk
- ▲ 1 ½ cups fat-free egg substitute
- 1 teaspoon vanilla extract
- ¼ teaspoon ground cinnamon
- Pinch salt
- ½ cup packed light brown sugar
- 2 tablespoons light stick butter, at room temperature
- ¼ cup pure maple syrup, warmed

1 Spray 8-inch square baking dish with nonstick spray.

2 Arrange bread in 4 equal stacks in baking dish (it will be tight). Whisk together milk, egg substitute, vanilla, cinnamon, and salt in medium bowl. Slowly pour egg mixture over bread; with pancake spatula, lightly press bread and spoon egg mixture over any uncoated bread. Cover and refrigerate up to 1 day.

3 Preheat oven to 350°F.

4 With fork, mix together brown sugar and butter in small bowl until smooth; spread evenly over bread. Bake French toast until knife inserted 1 inch from center comes out clean, about 1 hour. Let cool on wire rack about 20 minutes; cut into 6 portions. Place 1 piece of French toast on each of 6 plates and drizzle evenly with maple syrup.

 PER SERVING (1 piece French toast with 2 teaspoons syrup)

To make it a meal

Turn this French toast into a dish perfect for company by starting off with glasses of freshly squeezed orange juice garnished with fresh mint sprigs (4 ounces of fresh orange juice per serving will increase the *PointsPlus* value by **2**). Top each serving of French toast with sliced fresh strawberries and raspberries.

pla

n lunch

sandwiches, soups, and salads

Turkey-Pear Melt

Southwest-Style Chicken Wrap   SERVES 1

Spread **1 (7-inch) whole wheat tortilla** with **2 tablespoons prepared guacamole**. Top with **2 tablespoons fat-free salsa**, **¼ cup shredded fat-free Cheddar cheese**, **⅓ cup diced cooked chicken breast**, and **1 green leaf lettuce leaf**. Roll up tortilla to enclose filling.

To make it a meal

Sip a tall glass of lemon-mint iced tea with this satisfying wrap.

 Per serving (1 wrap)

Turkey-Pear Melt   SERVES 1

Preheat toaster oven broiler. Spread **1 (1-ounce) slice reduced-calorie whole wheat bread** with **1 teaspoon Dijon mustard**. Top with **1 (1-ounce) slice smoked turkey breast**, **½ thinly sliced pear**, and **2 tablespoons shredded fat-free mozzarella cheese**. Place sandwich on toaster oven tray; broil until cheese is melted, 2–3 minutes.

 Per serving (1 sandwich)

Ham 'n' Slaw Sammie   SERVES 1

Preheat toaster oven broiler. Mix together **¾ cup shredded cabbage**, **1 tablespoon thinly sliced red onion**, **1 table-spoon fat-free mayonnaise**, **1 teaspoon lemon juice**, and **1 teaspoon Dijon mustard** in small bowl. Put **¼ pound thinly sliced lean cooked ham** on **1 (1-ounce) slice toasted reduced-calorie bread**. Top with **1 (1-ounce) slice fat-free Swiss cheese**. Broil until cheese is melted, 1–2 minutes. Top with slaw.

 Per serving (1 sandwich)

Grilled Cheese and Ham   SERVES 1

Preheat panini press. Layer **1 slice lean cooked ham**, **½ cup loosely packed baby spinach**, and **¼ cup shredded fat-free mozzarella cheese** on half of **1 (10-inch) fat-free whole wheat tortilla**. Fold unfilled half of tortilla over to enclose filling. Place in panini press and cook until cheese is melted and tortilla is nicely marked, about 2 minutes.

 Per serving (1 sandwich)

To make it a meal

Place 2 or 3 thin slices of ripe tomato over the spinach for extra flavor. End your meal with a refreshing fat-free iced cappuccino sprinkled with un-sweetened cocoa. An 8-ounce cappuccino prepared with fat-free milk will increase the *PointsPlus* value by **1**.

Tomato-Watermelon Gazpacho   SERVES 1

Combine **1 coarsely chopped small tomato**, **¼ peeled and coarsely chopped cucumber**, **¾ cup cubed seedless watermelon**, **¼ seeded and minced jalapeño pepper**, and **2 teaspoons chopped fresh basil** in blender; blend until smooth. Add **2 teaspoons lime juice** and **pinch salt**; pulse until mixed well. Pour into soup bowl; refrigerate, covered, until well chilled, at least 3 hours or up to overnight. Serve sprinkled with **¼ thinly sliced scallion**.

 Per serving (generous 1 cup)

To make it a meal

Serve flavorful cooked shrimp—skewered if you like—alongside the gazpacho (3 ounces of cooked shrimp will increase the *PointsPlus* value by **2**).

Strawberry-Turkey Salad   SERVES 1

Mix together **2 cups spring salad mix**, **1 cup sliced straw-berries**, **¼ pound diced cooked turkey breast**, **1 table-spoon snipped fresh chives**, and **1 tablespoon chopped toasted almonds** in bowl. Add **1 tablespoon plus 1 teaspoon low-fat raspberry dressing**; toss until mixed well.

 Per serving (3 cups)

Super Spinach Toss   SERVES 1

Toss together **2 cups loosely packed baby spinach**, ⅔ cup **thawed frozen shelled edamame**, ½ **diced unpeeled red apple**, and ½ cup **shredded green cabbage** in medium bowl. Add **2 tablespoons fat-free ginger dressing**; toss until mixed well.

 Per serving (3 cups)

To make it a meal

Add a grated or chopped hard-cooked large egg to this lunchtime salad (1 large hard-cooked egg will increase the *PointsPlus* value by *2*).

Chicken and Cheese   SERVES 1

Toss together **1 ½ cups mixed baby kale or other baby lettuce, 1 cup diced cooked chicken breast**, ¼ **cup fat-free croutons**, and **1 tablespoon crumbled soft goat cheese** in medium bowl. Add **2 tablespoons fat-free balsamic dressing**; toss until mixed well.

 Per serving (2 ¾ cups)

To make it a meal

Bulk up this dish by tossing in a handful of halved cherry tomatoes, and end on a sweet note by enjoying ripe cherries or seedless grapes.

Crab and Slaw "Parfait"   SERVES 1

Toss together ¾ **cup loosely packed trimmed watercress**, ¾ **cup sliced escarole**, ⅓ **cup julienned celery root or Asian pear**, and **3 sliced kumquats (optional)** in medium bowl. Add **1 ½ tablespoons fat-free red-wine vinaigrette**; toss until mixed well. Alternately layer with **1 (6-ounce) can drained and picked-over crabmeat** in glass, forming three layers of salad and two layers of crabmeat.

 Per serving (2 ½ cups)

To make it a meal

End with chunks of ripe honeydew mixed with fresh raspberries and blackberries, as well as a tall glass of unsweetened iced coffee lightened with 2 tablespoons of fat-free half-and-half.

Thai Beef Salad

Thai Beef Salad SERVES 1

To make dressing, whisk together juice of **½ lime**, **½ teaspoon canola oil**, **½ teaspoon Asian fish sauce**, **½ teaspoon reduced-sodium soy sauce**, and **½ teaspoon honey** in small serving bowl until blended. Add **3 ounces sliced lean eye round roast beef, trimmed and cut into thin strips**, **¼ large bunch trimmed watercress**, **¼ cup loosely packed fresh mint leaves**, **¼ cup shredded carrot**, **scant ¼ cup loosely packed fresh cilantro leaves**, and **2 thinly sliced radishes**; toss until mixed well.

 Per serving (2 cups)

Italian Seafood Salad SERVES 1

Toss together **1 ½ cups thinly sliced romaine lettuce**, **1 cup diced cooked lobster meat**, **½ cup diced cooked beets**, and **¼ cup diced celery** in medium bowl. Add **2 tablespoons fat-free creamy Italian dressing**; toss until mixed well.

 Per serving (about 3 cups)

To make it a meal

Finish off lunch with a juicy piece of stone fruit of your choice along with a glass of unsweetened iced tea.

Panzanella Salad with Mozzarella SERVES 1

Toss together **1 diced large tomato**, **2 diced day-old slices reduced-calorie bread**, **⅔ cup peeled and diced cucumber**, **¼ cup thinly sliced red onion**, **6 torn fresh basil leaves**, and **1 ounce diced fat-free mozzarella cheese** in medium bowl. Add **2 tablespoons fat-free Italian dressing**; toss until mixed well.

 Per serving (2 cups)

To make it a meal

Add ¼ diced red bell pepper to the panzanella, and for dessert enjoy a wedge of ripe cantaloupe.

Saigon Sub

Chicken Burger on a Bun SERVES 1

Mix together **6 ounces ground skinless chicken breast**, **1 teaspoon Worcestershire sauce**, **¾ teaspoon balsamic vinegar**, and **¼ teaspoon dried thyme** in small bowl; shape into ½-inch-thick patty. Spray ridged grill pan with nonstick spray and set over medium heat. Add patty and cook until instant-read thermometer inserted into side of burger registers 160°F for well done, about 5 minutes per side. Place burger and **2 tomato slices** on bottom of **toasted light hamburger bun**; cover with top of bun.

To make it a meal

Top the burger with a leaf or two of green leaf lettuce along with a few thin slices of red or sweet white onion.

 Per serving (1 garnished burger)

Saigon Sub SERVES 1

To make slaw, whisk together **juice of ½ lime** and **1 teaspoon packed brown sugar** in medium bowl until sugar is dissolved. Stir in **¾ cup shredded red cabbage**, **¼ cup shredded carrot**, and **pinch salt**. Let stand, tossing occasionally, until cabbage is slightly wilted, about 30 minutes. Sprinkle **1 (3-ounce) lean boneless pork chop (¼ inch thick), trimmed**, with **pinch salt** and **pinch black pepper**. Spray small nonstick skillet with nonstick spray and set over medium heat. Add pork and cook until cooked through, about 1 ½ minutes per side. Remove soft center from **2 ½-ounce piece split whole wheat baguette**. Mix together **2 teaspoons low-fat mayonnaise** with **¼ teaspoon Sriracha or to taste**; use to spread over bottom of bread. Place **6 slices English (seedless) cucumber** and pork on top. Drain liquid from slaw; spoon on top of pork. Garnish with **2 fresh cilantro sprigs** and cover with top of bread.

 Per serving (1 sandwich)

Fish 'Wich" SERVES 1

Heat **1 teaspoon canola oil** in small nonstick skillet over medium heat. Add **⅓ cup diced onion** and **⅓ cup diced green and yellow bell pepper**; cook until onion is slightly softened, about 4 minutes. Add **¼ pound diced haddock fillet** and sprinkle with **½ teaspoon smoked paprika**; cook until fragrant, about 1 minute. Stir in **⅓ cup barbecue sauce**; cook, stirring, until fish is cooked through about 2 minutes longer. Spoon fish mixture onto **1 split light hamburger bun**.

 Per serving (1 sandwich)

To make it a meal

Enjoy a mixed green salad topped with your favorite fat-free salad dressing alongside this easy and satisfying fish sandwich.

Cold Cucumber Soup with Crabmeat

SERVES 1

To make soup, combine **¼ peeled and chopped English (seedless) cucumber** and **⅓ cup vegetable broth** in blender; blend until smooth. Pour into small metal bowl; whisk in **⅓ cup plain fat-free yogurt**, **small pinch salt**, and **pinch black pepper**. Cover and refrigerate until cold, at least 2 hours or up to overnight. To make croutons, heat **1 teaspoon olive oil** in small nonstick skillet over medium heat. Add **1 thinly sliced small garlic clove** and **½ cubed slice whole wheat reduced-calorie bread**; cook, stirring frequently, until bread is golden, about 6 minutes. Let cool. Ladle cold soup into soup bowl; top with **1 ½ ounces canned crabmeat, preferably lump, drained and picked over**. Sprinkle croutons on top.

 Per serving (about 1 cup soup with about 3 tablespoons crabmeat and ⅓ cup croutons)

To make it a meal

Start with a salad of sliced ripe tomatoes layered with thinly sliced fat-free mozzarella cheese and sprinkled with torn fresh basil (1 ounce of thinly sliced fat-free mozzarella cheese will increase the *PointsPlus* value by *1*).

Broccoli Chowder

Broccoli Chowder SERVES 1

Heat **1 teaspoon canola oil** in small saucepan over medium heat. Add **⅓ cup chopped onion**, **1 teaspoon minced garlic**, and **¼ teaspoon dried thyme**; cook, stirring, until onion is softened, about 3 minutes. Stir in **½ cup chicken broth**, **⅓ cup no-salt-added cream-style corn**, **⅓ cup thawed frozen chopped broccoli**, and **¼ cup fat-free half-and-half**. Bring just to boil.

 Per serving (1 ¾ cups)

To make it a meal

Serve the chowder with a salad of sliced tomato and cucumber along with 3 ounces of thinly sliced smoked turkey breast. This will increase the *PointsPlus* value by *2*.

Tex-Mex Pinto Bean Soup SERVES 1

Combine **1 ½ cups reduced-sodium vegetable broth**, **½ diced small zucchini**, **¼ cup rinsed and drained pinto beans**, **¼ cup frozen corn kernels**, **2 thinly sliced scallions**, **1 tablespoon fat-free salsa**, **1 teaspoon lime juice**, and **½ teaspoon chili powder** in small saucepan; bring to boil. Reduce heat; simmer, covered, until zucchini is tender and flavors are blended, about 5 minutes. Ladle soup into soup bowl. Top with **1 tablespoon chopped fresh cilantro** and croutons made from **½ slice toasted reduced-calorie bread**.

Per serving (about 2 cups)

Mushroom Miso Soup   SERVES 1

Heat **¼ teaspoon canola oil** with **¼ teaspoon Asian (dark) sesame oil** in small saucepan over medium heat. Add **½ cup sliced cremini mushrooms** and cook, stirring, until slightly softened, about 1 minute. Stir in **1 ½ cups reduced-sodium vegetable broth** and **2 teaspoons white or yellow miso**; bring to boil. Stir in **½ pound sliced bok choy** and **¼ pound diced silken tofu**; reduce heat and simmer until bok choy is tender, about 4 minutes longer.

 Per serving (2 ½ cups)

To make it a meal

Begin with a romaine lettuce and cherry tomato salad dressed with fat-free carrot-ginger salad dressing, and end with fresh lychees or canned unsweetened mandarin orange segments to keep the Asian theme going.

Crunchy Chicken Salad   SERVES 1

To make dressing, whisk together **2 teaspoons red-wine vinegar**, **1 ½ teaspoons extra-virgin olive oil**, **pinch salt**, and **pinch black pepper** in medium bowl. Add **4 trimmed and sliced large radishes**, **½ cup shredded cooked chicken breast**, **¼ thinly sliced peeled, halved, and seeded cucumber**, **1 thinly sliced celery stalk**, **6 thinly sliced fresh basil leaves**, and **1 finely chopped small shallot**; toss until mixed well. Stir in **1 cup loosely packed mixed baby salad greens**. Toss until combined well.

 Per serving (about 2 cups)

Spinach, Shrimp, and Egg Salad   SERVES 1

Heat **2 teaspoons olive oil** in small nonstick skillet over medium heat. Add **1 chopped small shallot** and cook, stirring, 2 minutes. Add **2 tablespoons balsamic vinegar** and simmer until shallot is softened, about 3 minutes longer. Toss warm dressing, **3 ounces cooked large shrimp**, **2 cups loosely packed baby spinach**, and **1 chopped hard-cooked large egg** in medium bowl until mixed well.

 Per serving (2 cups)

To make it a meal

Add 3 or 4 sliced white mushrooms and 1 slice of toasted reduced-calorie rye bread cut into croutons to the salad.

Portobello Salad   SERVES 1

Preheat broiler. Brush **1 large portobello mushroom cap** with **1 tablespoon fat-free creamy Italian dressing**. Place on broiler rack and broil 5 inches from heat until tender, about 2 minutes per side. Let cool 2 minutes; thickly slice. Toss together **1 ½ cups loosely packed mixed salad greens**, **3 ounces cooked lean ham, cut into strips**, and **¼ cup thinly sliced red onion rings** in serving bowl; top with mushroom and drizzle with **1 tablespoon fat-free creamy Italian dressing**.

Per serving (2 cups)

Tortellini en Brodo

Tortellini en Brodo SERVES 4

▲ 1 (32-ounce) carton reduced-sodium chicken broth

2 (2 ½-inch) strips lemon zest

1 (9-ounce) package refrigerated three-cheese tortellini

▲ 1 ½ cups frozen baby peas

1 teaspoon salt

¼ teaspoon black pepper

2 tablespoons grated Parmesan cheese

1 tablespoon finely chopped fresh flat-leaf parsley

1 Combine broth and lemon zest in large saucepan and bring to boil. Stir in tortellini; cover and return to boil. Reduce heat and simmer, uncovered, 8 minutes.

2 Stir peas, salt, and pepper into saucepan; simmer until tortellini is tender and peas are heated through, about 2 minutes. Discard lemon zest. Ladle soup into 4 bowls. Sprinkle with Parmesan and parsley.

 Per serving (about 2 cups)

To make it a meal

Add dark leafy greens—Swiss chard, spinach, and mustard greens are all good choices—to this simple soup for a good-for-you dose of potassium, magnesium, vitamin A, and antioxidants. Thinly slice a handful or two of the greens and add to the soup along with the peas in step 2.

cook it
in more time

Mushroom, Beef, and Barley Soup SERVES 4

▲ 1 (32-ounce) carton reduced-sodium beef broth

  1 cup water

▲ ½ cup quick-cooking barley

  2 teaspoons canola oil

▲ 2 leeks, sliced (white and light green parts only)

▲ 1 carrot, chopped

▲ ¾ pound boneless lean sirloin steak, trimmed and cut into ½-inch pieces

  3 garlic cloves, minced

  ½ teaspoon pumpkin pie spice

▲ ¾ pound oyster or cremini mushrooms, sliced

▲ ¼ pound shiitake mushrooms, stemmed and caps thinly sliced

▲ 2 cups loosely packed chopped kale leaves

To make it a meal

For dessert, serve thinly sliced fresh strawberries mixed with diced fresh pineapple.

1 Bring broth, water, and barley to boil in large Dutch oven. Reduce heat and simmer, covered, until barley is tender, about 12 minutes.

2 Meanwhile, heat oil in large nonstick skillet over medium heat. Add leeks and carrot; cook, stirring frequently, until leeks are softened, about 5 minutes. Add beef and cook, stirring occasionally, until browned, about 5 minutes. Add garlic and pumpkin pie spice; cook, stirring frequently, until fragrant, about 30 seconds. Add mushrooms and cook, stirring occasionally, until softened, about 6 minutes longer.

3 Stir mushroom mixture and kale into broth mixture. Reduce heat and simmer, covered, until kale is tender, about 5 minutes.

 Per serving (1 ¾ cups)

Chilled Veggie Soup SERVES 4

- ▲ 2 ¼ cups reduced-sodium chicken broth
- ▲ 1 ½ cups fresh or frozen shelled edamame, thawed
-   1 cup water
- ▲ 3 scallions, sliced
- ▲ 1 celery stalk, diced
-   ¼ teaspoon salt
-   ⅛ teaspoon black pepper
- ▲ ½ pound sugar snap peas, trimmed and sliced
-   ¼ cup loosely packed fresh mint leaves, finely chopped
- ▲ 4 teaspoons fat-free half-and-half

1 Combine broth, edamame, water, scallions, celery, salt, and pepper in large saucepan; bring to boil. Reduce heat and simmer, covered, until edamame and celery are tender, about 10 minutes. Add sugar snap peas and return to boil. Reduce heat and simmer, covered, until peas are crisp-tender, about 2 minutes longer. Remove from heat; let soup cool about 5 minutes.

2 Puree soup in batches in blender. Transfer puree to large bowl. Put 1 tablespoon mint in cup; cover and refrigerate until ready to serve. Stir remaining 3 tablespoons mint into soup. Let soup cool to room temperature, stirring occasionally, about 30 minutes. Cover soup and refrigerate until cold, at least 3 hours or up to overnight.

3 Ladle soup into 4 bowls. Drizzle each serving with 1 teaspoon half-and-half, swirling with tip of small knife to marble. Sprinkle soup with remaining 1 tablespoon mint.

 Per serving (1 cup)

Moroccan Split Pea Soup SERVES 6

1 ½ teaspoons canola oil

▲ 1 large onion, chopped

3 garlic cloves, minced

1 tablespoon ground coriander

1 tablespoon ground cumin

▲ 2 (32-ounce) cartons reduced-sodium chicken broth

▲ 1 (16-ounce) bag yellow split peas, picked over, rinsed, and drained

▲ ¾ cup canned chickpeas, rinsed and drained

▲ 1 (14 ½-ounce) can diced tomatoes

To make it a meal

Bulk up this exotic-tasting soup by adding diced peeled all-purpose potatoes along with the split peas in step 2 (1 pound raw all-purpose potatoes will increase the per-serving *PointsPlus* value by *1*).

1 Heat oil in large saucepan over medium heat. Add onion and cook, stirring, until softened, about 5 minutes. Add garlic, coriander, and cumin; cook, stirring frequently, until fragrant, about 1 minute longer.

2 Stir in broth and split peas; bring to boil. Reduce heat and simmer, covered, until split peas are softened, about 1 hour.

3 Transfer 2 cups of split pea mixture to blender and blend until smooth. Stir puree, chickpeas, and tomatoes into saucepan; cook, covered, until soup is heated through and flavors are blended, about 15 minutes. Ladle soup into 6 bowls.

 Per serving (about 1 ⅓ cups)

Moroccan Split Pea Soup

ake
dinner

meat, poultry, fish, and vegetarian

Beef and Blue Cheese Salad   SERVES 1

Combine **1 ½ cups loosely packed torn red leaf lettuce,
1 cup (2-inch lengths) asparagus, ¼ pound sliced lean
eye round roast beef, trimmed and cut into strips,** and
½ ounce bagel chips (about 7), broken up, in medium bowl.
Drizzle with **2 tablespoons low-fat blue cheese dressing**;
toss until mixed well.

 **Per serving (3 cups)**

Steak Kebabs   SERVES 1

Place toaster oven tray in toaster oven and preheat broiler.
Stir together **1 (¼-pound) lean filet mignon, trimmed
and cut into 6 cubes, 2 teaspoons olive oil, ½ teaspoon
grated lime zest, ¼ teaspoon crushed fennel seeds,
¼ teaspoon ground cumin, ⅛ teaspoon ground
coriander,** and **⅛ teaspoon dried oregano** in small bowl.
Thread beef and **¼ red bell pepper, cut into 4 pieces**, onto
2 small metal skewers. Place in tray and broil until beef is
cooked to medium doneness, 2–3 minutes per side.

 **Per serving (2 kebabs)**

To make it a meal

For dessert have
a crisp apple cut
into wedges along
with sliced fat-free
Cheddar cheese. A
1-ounce slice of fat-
free Cheddar cheese
will increase the
PointsPlus value
by **1**.

Citrus Ham Salad   SERVES 1

Combine **2 cups loosely packed torn romaine lettuce leaves**, **1 cup blood orange sections**, **½ cup lean cooked ham strips**, and **1 ½ teaspoons toasted pumpkin seeds** in medium bowl. Drizzle with **2 tablespoons low-fat honey mustard dressing**; toss until mixed well.

 Per serving (3 cups)

To make it a meal

End with a dish of plain fat-free Greek yogurt topped with fresh berries (½ cup of plain fat-free Greek yogurt will increase the *PointsPlus* value by *1*).

Chicken Fruit Cup   SERVES 1

Mix together **1 cup cantaloupe balls**, **¾ cup diced store-bought grilled or roasted chicken breast**, **¼ cup diced celery**, and **scant 1 tablespoon chopped fresh mint** in medium bowl. Scoop out center from **½ small head iceberg lettuce (about 6 ounces)**; fill with fruit mixture. Drizzle with **2 tablespoons fat-free poppy seed dressing**.

 Per serving (1 filled lettuce cup)

Blueberry-Peach Turkey Salad   SERVES 1

Whisk together **1 ½ teaspoons lemon juice**, **1 ½ teaspoons honey**, **½ teaspoon extra-virgin olive oil**, and **¼ teaspoon chopped fresh thyme** in medium bowl. Add **¾ cup diced cooked turkey breast**, **1 cup loosely packed baby arugula**, **⅓ cup fresh blueberries**, and **1 sliced peach**; toss until mixed well.

 Per serving (2 cups)

**Summer Salad
Kebabs**

Summer Salad Kebabs   SERVES 1

Alternately thread **2 cups iceberg lettuce chunks,
1 nectarine cut into wedges**, **1 cup grilled or steamed
baby zucchini and patty pan squash**, **⅔ cup chunks lean
cooked ham**, and **¼ cup red onion pieces** onto 2 wooden
skewers. Drizzle evenly with **2 tablespoons fat-free
Thousand Island dressing.**

 Per serving (2 kebabs)

Thai Tuna   SERVES 1

Mix together **1 ½ teaspoons reduced-sodium soy sauce,
½ teaspoon ground cumin, ½ teaspoon packed brown
sugar, ½ teaspoon Asian (dark) sesame oil,** and **pinch
cayenne** in glass pie plate. Add **1 (5-ounce) tuna steak** and
turn to coat. Let stand 5 minutes. Cover pie plate with wax
paper; microwave on High until tuna is pink in center, about
1 ½ minutes. Sprinkle with **1 sliced small scallion**. Cover and
microwave until tuna is barely pink in center and scallion
is softened, about 1 ½ minutes longer. Let stand 1 minute
before serving.

 Per serving (1 tuna steak)

Microwave Greek Salmon SERVES 1

Place **thin slices of ½ lemon** in one layer in small microwavable dish; top with **1 (6-ounce) wild salmon fillet**. Sprinkle with **¼ teaspoon dried oregano**; add **2 tablespoons water** to dish. Cover dish with wax paper; microwave on High just until fish is opaque in center, 5–6 min.

 Per serving (1 salmon fillet)

To make it a meal

Red or white quinoa and steamed whole green beans sprinkled with lemon juice nicely complement this Greek-influenced fish dish (½ cup of cooked quinoa will increase the **PointsPlus** value by **3**).

Tilapia Italiano SERVES 1

Preheat toaster oven to 375°F. Spray toaster oven tray with nonstick spray. Wrap **1 (1-ounce) slice lean cooked ham** around **1 (5-ounce) tilapia fillet**. Place on toaster oven tray. Scatter **1 cup cherry tomatoes** around fish and drizzle fish and tomatoes with **1 teaspoon extra-virgin olive oil**. Sprinkle tomatoes with **¼ teaspoon dried oregano**, **pinch salt**, and **pinch black pepper**. Bake until fish is just opaque in center and tomatoes are softened, about 12 minutes.

 Per serving (1 tilapia fillet with ¾ cup cherry tomatoes)

To make it a meal

To continue the Italian theme, start your meal off with a classic arugula, radicchio, and fennel salad dressed with lemon juice. Then serve the tilapia with brown rice and spoon some of the cooked cherry tomatoes and juice on top (½ cup of cooked brown rice will increase the **PointsPlus** value by **3**).

Ginger, Tofu, and Veggie Salad

Peachy Crab Salad   SERVES 1

Mix together **5 ounces lump crabmeat, picked over, 1 diced peach, 1 minced shallot,** and **½ teaspoon seeded and minced jalapeño pepper** in medium bowl. Mix together **1 ½ teaspoons canola oil, ½ teaspoon curry powder,** and **¼ teaspoon ground cumin** in cup. Microwave on High until hot, about 30 seconds; stir well and let stand 10 seconds. Add to crab mixture and stir until mixed well. Place **1 cup loosely packed baby arugula** on plate. Top with crab mixture.

To make it a meal

Begin with half of a medium red grapefruit, and serve a slice of light rye bread alongside the crab salad. This will increase the *PointsPlus* value by *3*.

 Per serving (1 ¾ cups)

Ginger, Tofu, and Veggie Salad   SERVES 1

Combine **2 cups loosely packed baby spinach, ½ cup shredded carrots, ½ cup thinly sliced red bell pepper, ¼ pound firm tofu, grilled and cubed,** and **2 sliced radishes** in medium bowl. Drizzle with **2 tablespoons fat-free ginger dressing**; toss until mixed well.

 Per serving (3 ⅓ cups)

**Pork Chops with
Fennel and Peppers**

Pork Chops with Fennel and Peppers

SERVES 1

Sprinkle **1 (5-ounce) lean bone-in rib pork chop (about 1 inch thick), trimmed** with **1 teaspoon chopped fresh rosemary**, **pinch salt**, and **pinch black pepper**. Heat **¾ teaspoon olive oil** in small nonstick skillet over medium heat. Add pork and cook until lightly browned and cooked through, 5–6 minutes per side. Transfer to plate; cover and keep warm. Dice **½ cup fennel bulb**; chop **1 tablespoon fronds**. Add diced fennel and **½ cup diced yellow bell pepper** to skillet, cook over medium heat, stirring occasionally, until vegetables are softened, about 5 minutes. Stir in **¼ cup canned tomato sauce**, **1 tablespoon golden raisins**, and **½ teaspoon red-wine vinegar**; bring to boil. Cook until mixture is slightly thickened, about 2 minutes. Sprinkle vegetables with fennel fronds; serve with pork chop.

To make it a meal
A ½ cup of cooked polenta will up the *PointsPlus* value by *3*.

 Per serving (1 pork chop with about ½ cup vegetables)

Crispy Cabbage and Pork Stir-Fry SERVES 1

Heat **1 teaspoon canola oil** in deep medium skillet or wok over medium-high heat. Add **¼ pound lean boneless pork chop, trimmed and cut into strips**; stir-fry 2 minutes. Add **1 ½ cups coleslaw mix**, **½ cup sliced bell pepper**, **1 minced garlic clove**, **2 teaspoons reduced-sodium soy sauce**, and **⅛ teaspoon black pepper**; stir-fry until vegetables are softened and pork is cooked through, about 3 minutes.

 Per serving (1 ½ cups)

Asian Steak with Bok Choy SERVES 1

Combine **¾ teaspoon reduced-sodium soy sauce**, **½ teaspoon grated lime zest**, and **1 minced small garlic clove** in small zip-close plastic bag. Add **¼ pound trimmed and thinly sliced lean sirloin steak**. Squeeze out air and seal bag; turn to coat steak. Refrigerate, turning bag occasionally, 30 minutes. Meanwhile, to make dressing, whisk together **juice of ½ lime**, **1 minced small garlic clove**, **¼ teaspoon sugar**, and **pinch red pepper flakes** in medium bowl. Add **1 cup thinly sliced bok choy**, **1 cup shredded Napa cabbage**, and **1 thinly sliced small shallot** to dressing in bowl (do not mix). Spray deep medium skillet or wok with nonstick spray and set over medium-high heat. Add steak mixture and stir-fry until beef is browned, 1–2 minutes. Add steak to bok choy mixture in bowl; toss until mixed well.

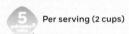 Per serving (2 cups)

To make it a meal

Serve this flavorful Asian dish over brown rice and sprinkle with thinly sliced scallion (½ cup of cooked brown rice will increase the **PointsPlus** value by **3**). And for dessert enjoy 1 or 2 clementines.

Beef and Vegetable Ragu SERVES 1

Spray medium nonstick skillet with nonstick spray and set over medium heat. Add **3 ounces ground beef (5% fat or less)** and **2 tablespoons finely chopped onion**; cook, stirring, until beef is browned, about 3 minutes. Drain off any fat. Put **4 white mushrooms** in food processor; pulse until finely chopped. Add mushrooms and **½ cup diced unpeeled eggplant** to skillet; cook, stirring occasionally, until eggplant is browned, about 5 minutes. Stir in **1 minced garlic clove** and cook, stirring, until fragrant, about 1 minute. Stir in **¾ cup canned peeled whole plum tomatoes, broken up**, **1 teaspoon red-wine vinegar**, **¼ teaspoon dried oregano**, and **scant ¼ teaspoon salt**; bring to boil. Cook, stirring occasionally, until sauce is thickened, about 8 minutes longer.

 Per serving (about 1 cup)

To make it a meal

Serve the ragu over whole wheat pasta (1 cup of cooked whole wheat pasta will increase the **PointsPlus** value by **4**).

Grilled Lamb Chops with Pomegranate Sauce SERVES 1

To make sauce, coat small nonstick skillet with **½ teaspoon olive oil** and set over medium heat. Add **1 minced small garlic clove** and **pinch dried rosemary**; cook, stirring, until fragrant, about 30 seconds. Add **¼ cup pomegranate juice** and bring to boil; cook until reduced by half, about 3 minutes. Whisk together **2 tablespoons reduced-sodium chicken broth**, **¾ teaspoon balsamic vinegar**, and **½ teaspoon cornstarch** in cup until smooth; pour into skillet. Return sauce to boil, stirring constantly. Reduce heat and simmer until thickened, 1–2 minutes. Remove skillet from heat; cover and keep warm. Sprinkle **1 (6-ounce) bone-in loin lamb chop (about ¾ inch thick), trimmed**, with **pinch salt** and **pinch black pepper**; spray both sides with nonstick spray. Heat nonstick ridged grill pan over medium heat. Put lamb in pan and grill until instant-read thermometer inserted into side of chop registers 145°F for medium, about 4 minutes per side. Serve with sauce.

 Per serving (1 lamb chop with 2 tablespoons sauce)

Lamb Burger SERVES 1

Mix together **¼ pound ground trimmed lean leg of lamb**, **1 teaspoon fat-free mayonnaise**, **¼ teaspoon Dijon mustard**, and **¼ teaspoon Worcestershire sauce**. With damp hands, shape into ½-inch-thick patty. Spray nonstick ridged grill pan with nonstick spray and set over medium heat. Place patty in pan and grill until instant-read thermometer inserted into side of burger registers 160°F for well done, about 4 minutes per side. Place burger in **1 split light hamburger bun**.

 Per serving (1 burger with bun)

To make it a meal

Put a red or green lettuce leaf on the bottom of the bun, then layer with thinly sliced cucumber, tomato, and onion. Place the burger and thinly sliced fat-free feta cheese on top (1 ounce fat-free feta cheese will increase the *PointsPlus* value by *1*).

Mustard-Almond Chicken SERVES 1

Mix together **4 teaspoons honey mustard** and **pinch cayenne** in cup; reserve 1 teaspoon. To make sauce, add **1 tablespoon light sour cream** and **½ teaspoon dried thyme** to mustard mixture in cup. Heat **1 teaspoon canola oil** in small nonstick skillet over medium heat. Add 1 (5-ounce) skinless boneless chicken breast; cook until cooked through, about 4 minutes per side. Spread reserved mustard mixture over top of chicken and sprinkle with **1 tablespoon sliced almonds**. Serve with sauce.

 Per serving (1 chicken breast with almonds and 2 tablespoons sauce)

To make it a meal

Begin your dinner with cooked shrimp drizzled with lemon juice and served with your favorite hot sauce (3 ounces of cooked shrimp will increase the *PointsPlus* value by **2**).

Tex-Mex Chicken Tacos SERVES 1

Stir together **¼ teaspoon dried oregano**, **¼ teaspoon ground coriander**, **¼ teaspoon ground cumin**, **½ teaspoon grated lime zest**, and **pinch salt** in small bowl. Add 1 (5-ounce) skinless boneless chicken breast, cut crosswise into ½-inch strips; toss to coat. Coat medium nonstick skillet with **½ teaspoon canola oil** and set over medium heat. Add chicken and cook, stirring frequently, until cooked through, about 5 minutes. With slotted spoon, transfer chicken to medium bowl. Add **½ teaspoon oil** to skillet. Add ½ thinly sliced small onion, ⅓ cup thinly sliced yellow bell pepper, ⅓ cup thinly sliced red bell pepper, **1 thinly sliced small garlic clove**, and **pinch salt** to skillet. Cook, tossing frequently, until vegetables are crisp-tender, about 5 minutes. Transfer vegetables to bowl with chicken; add **2 teaspoons lime juice** and toss until mixed well. Spoon into **warm 7-inch fat-free flour tortilla**.

 Per serving (1 tortilla with 1 ½ cups filling)

Chicken and Corn Salad   SERVES 1

Remove kernels from **1 ear of corn, husk and silk removed.**
Combine corn with **1 tablespoon water** in shallow microwavable casserole. Cover dish with paper towel and microwave
on High until corn is crisp-tender, 1 ½–2 minutes. Meanwhile,
whisk together **½ teaspoon olive oil**, **½ teaspoon balsamic
vinegar**, and **pinch salt** in medium bowl. With slotted spoon,
transfer corn to bowl with dressing. Stir in **⅔ cup diced
cooked chicken breast**, **¼ cup tiny red and yellow tomatoes**, **¼ cup thinly sliced red onion**, and **4 chopped large
fresh basil leaves**; toss until mixed well.

To make it a meal

Enjoy a second ear of
corn for an additional
PointsPlus value of **2**.

 Per serving (about 1 ⅓ cups)

Crispy Fish and Chips   SERVES 1

Preheat oven to 425°F. Line two small rimmed baking pans
with nonstick foil or parchment paper. Mix together **1 ½
tablespoons all-purpose flour**, **⅛ teaspoon salt**, and **pinch
black pepper** in shallow bowl. Beat **1 large egg white** and
1 tablespoon water in another shallow bowl. Spread **⅓ cup
cornflake crumbs** on sheet of wax paper. Cut **1 (4-ounce)
scrubbed sweet potato into 6 wedges**. Working with a few
wedges at a time, dip potato into flour mixture, then into
egg white mixture, allowing excess to drip off. Coat wedges
with crumbs, pressing so they adhere. Place potato wedges
in single layer on baking sheet; bake 10 minutes. Meanwhile
flour, dip, and coat **1 (¼-pound) tilapia fillet** with remaining
flour, egg white, and crumbs; place on second baking sheet.
After potatoes have baked 10 minutes, put tilapia into oven.
Bake until fish is just opaque in center and sweet potatoes
are crisp and fork-tender, 10–12 minutes. Serve fish and chips
with **lemon wedge** and **1 tablespoon low-sugar ketchup**.

 Per serving (1 fish fillet with 6 chips and 1 tablespoon ketchup)

Shrimp and Scallops Veracruz   SERVES 1

Mix together **2 ounces peeled and deveined large shrimp**, **2 ounces sea scallops**, **2 teaspoons lime juice**, and **pinch salt** in small bowl. Cover and refrigerate 30 minutes. Spray medium nonstick skillet with nonstick spray and set over medium heat. Add **¼ cup chopped onion** and cook, stirring, until softened, about 5 minutes. Add **1 minced garlic clove** and **¼ teaspoon dried oregano**; cook, stirring, until fragrant, about 45 seconds. Add **½ cup canned crushed tomatoes**, **3 tablespoons pitted and quartered green olives**, and **1–2 teaspoons chopped pickled jalapeño pepper plus 1 teaspoon pickling juice**; bring to boil, stirring occasionally. Stir in shrimp, scallops, and pinch salt. Reduce heat and simmer, covered, until seafood is just opaque in center, about 7 minutes.

To make it a meal
A bed of brown rice is the perfect way to ensure you get to taste every bit of this saucy robust dish (½ cup of cooked brown rice will increase the *PointsPlus* value by *3*).

 Per serving (about ¾ cup)

Veggie Fettuccine with Tomatoes   SERVES 1

With swivel-blade vegetable peeler, peel **1 small green zucchini** and **1 small golden zucchini** lengthwise into ¾-inch-wide strips, avoiding seeded center. Discard centers. Combine zucchini and **½ cup matchstick-cut carrot** in colander; toss with **pinch salt**. Let stand 30 minutes. Rinse vegetables under cold water and drain; pat dry with paper towels and transfer to medium bowl. Mix together **1 seeded and diced tomato**, **1 tablespoon chopped fresh cilantro**, **2 teaspoons extra-virgin olive oil**, **1 minced small garlic clove**, **¼ teaspoon dried oregano**, and **¼ seeded and minced jalapeño pepper** in medium bowl. Top vegetables with tomato mixture and sprinkle with **3 tablespoons crumbled fat-free feta cheese**.

To make it a meal
Aromatic garlic bread makes a great accompaniment to this meatless dish. Toast a slice of reduced-calorie bread, then rub garlic on one side of the bread and lightly spray with olive oil nonstick spray (1 slice of reduced-calorie bread will increase the *PointsPlus* value by *1*).

 Per serving (1 ⅓ cups)

Green Chile Enchiladas   SERVES 1

Put **1 ½ cups loosely packed washed Swiss chard, cut into thin strips**, with water still clinging to leaves, in small nonstick skillet and set over medium heat. Cook, stirring, until chard is wilted and liquid is evaporated, about 2 minutes. Transfer to plate. Spray skillet with nonstick spray. Add **2 tablespoons chopped onion** and **1 minced garlic clove**; cook, stirring, until onion is softened, about 5 minutes. Remove skillet from heat; stir in **½ cup canned no-salt-added black beans, rinsed and drained**, **2 tablespoons shredded fat-free jalapeño soy cheese**, **pinch ground cumin**, and **pinch salt**. Lay **2 small corn tortillas** on work surface; layer each with half of chard and bean mixtures. Roll tortillas up to enclose filling. Bring **⅓ cup fat-free salsa verde** to simmer in skillet over medium heat. Place enchiladas, seam side down, in skillet; spoon salsa over top. Sprinkle evenly with **2 tablespoons shredded fat-free jalapeño soy cheese**. Reduce heat and simmer, covered, until filling is heated through and cheese is melted, about 5 minutes. Let stand 5 minutes before serving.

 Per serving (2 enchiladas)

Green Chile Enchiladas

Steaks Rouge

Steaks Rouge   SERVES 4

2 garlic cloves, coarsely chopped

1 ¼ teaspoons kosher salt

¾ teaspoon dried thyme

¼ teaspoon black pepper

▲ 4 (¼-pound) lean boneless sirloin steaks, trimmed

1 tablespoon olive oil

⅓ cup balsamic vinegar

▲ ¾ cup reduced-sodium chicken broth

▲ 2 plum tomatoes, diced

1 tablespoon cold water

1 ½ teaspoons cornstarch

1 gherkin or cornichon, finely diced

2 teaspoons capers, drained

1 teaspoon prepared horseradish

1 teaspoon Dijon mustard

To make it a meal

Add some fiber by serving the steaks with a side of cooked lentils and steamed asparagus (½ cup of cooked lentils per serving will increase the **PointsPlus** value by **2**).

1 Sprinkle garlic with 1 teaspoon of salt and chop until mixture forms paste. Stir in thyme and pepper. Spread garlic mixture over both sides of steaks. Place steaks on plate; cover with plastic wrap. Refrigerate at least 30 minutes or up to 2 hours.

2 Heat oil in large nonstick skillet over medium heat. Add steaks, in batches if needed, and cook until instant-read thermometer inserted into side of steak registers 145°F for medium, about 2 minutes per side. Transfer steaks to 4 plates and keep warm.

3 Add vinegar to skillet and bring to boil over medium heat. Stir in broth and tomatoes; cook, stirring occasionally, until mixture returns to boil.

4 Meanwhile, stir together water and cornstarch in cup until smooth. Whisk cornstarch mixture and remaining ¼ teaspoon salt into tomato mixture; cook, stirring frequently, until sauce bubbles and is slightly thickened, about 1 minute. Stir in gherkin, capers, horseradish, and mustard; bring to simmer. Spoon sauce over steaks.

 Per serving (1 sirloin steak and about 5 tablespoons sauce)

Brisket with Glazed Root Vegetables

SERVES 8

3 tablespoons all-purpose flour

1 cup dry red wine

▲ ½ cup reduced-sodium beef broth

2 tablespoons tomato paste

1 tablespoon packed brown sugar

3 large garlic cloves, minced

1 teaspoon dried thyme

1 (1-ounce) envelope dried onion-and-dip mix

1 teaspoon smoked paprika

½ teaspoon salt

½ teaspoon black pepper

1 (3-pound) lean first-cut brisket, trimmed

▲ 1 ½ pounds rutabaga, peeled and cut into chunks

▲ 8 large carrots, cut crosswise into thirds

1 Preheat oven to 325°F.

2 Put 1 tablespoon of flour in large oven-cooking bag; shake to coat bag. Put bag in large roasting pan. Whisk together wine, broth, remaining 2 tablespoons flour, the tomato paste, brown sugar, garlic, and thyme in 2-cup glass measure. Stir in onion soup-and-dip mix.

3 Stir together paprika, salt, and pepper in cup; rub all over brisket. Place brisket in center of oven bag. Put half of rutabaga in end of bag farthest from opening and remaining rutabaga along one long side of bag; put carrots on opposite long side. Pour wine mixture into bag; close with nylon tie. Cut 6 (½-inch) slits in top of bag.

4 Bake until brisket is fork-tender, about 3 hours. Let stand in bag 10 minutes. Cut top of bag open; transfer brisket and vegetables to platter. Cover loosely with foil and let stand 10 minutes. Pour sauce from bag into fat separator or glass measure; remove fat. Cut brisket across grain into 24 slices. Serve with vegetables and sauce.

 Per serving (3 slices brisket with about 1 cup vegetables and 3 ½ tablespoons sauce)

Pork with Tomato, Orange, and Olive Relish   SERVES 4

1 ½ tablespoons packed brown sugar

1 ½ teaspoons ground cumin

1 ½ teaspoons fennel seeds, crushed

1 teaspoon salt

¾ teaspoon coarsely ground pepper

3 teaspoons olive oil

▲ 1 (1-pound) lean pork tenderloin, trimmed

2 garlic cloves, minced

Grated zest and juice of 1 orange

▲ 1 (14 ½-ounce) can petite diced tomatoes, drained

½ cup green olives, pitted and quartered

To make it a meal

Serve steamed ears of fresh farmers' market corn alongside this flavorful main dish (1 steamed medium ear of corn for each serving will increase the **PointsPlus** value by **2**).

1 Preheat oven to 450°F.

2 Mix together brown sugar, cumin, fennel, ½ teaspoon of salt, and ½ teaspoon of pepper in small bowl. Rub 1 teaspoon of oil all over pork; coat with spice mixture.

3 Heat 1 teaspoon oil in large nonstick skillet over medium heat. Add pork and cook until browned on all sides, about 8 minutes. Transfer pork to 9 x 13-inch roasting pan or baking dish. Roast until instant-read thermometer inserted into center of pork registers 145°F for medium, about 20 minutes, turning pork once. Transfer to cutting board and cover pork loosely with foil; let stand 10 minutes.

4 Meanwhile, to make relish, heat remaining 1 teaspoon oil in same skillet over medium heat. Add garlic and orange zest; cook, stirring, until fragrant, about 45 seconds. Add orange juice and bring to boil. Cook, scraping up browned bits from bottom of pan, until mixture is reduced by half, about 3 minutes. Add tomatoes and cook until slightly thickened, about 2 minutes. Stir in olives and remaining ½ teaspoon salt and ¼ teaspoon pepper.

5 Cut pork into 12 slices. Add pork and any accumulated juices to skillet; turn to coat with sauce. Reduce heat and cook just until pork is heated through, 1–2 minutes.

 Per serving (3 slices pork with about ⅓ cup sauce)

Grilled Chicken and Corn Kebabs SERVES 4

▲ ¼ cup plain fat-free yogurt

¼ cup whole grain mustard

Juice of ½ lemon

3 large garlic cloves, minced

½ teaspoon salt

¼ teaspoon black pepper

▲ 1 pound skinless boneless chicken breasts, cut into 16 pieces

2 large lemons, each cut into 8 slices

16 fresh bay leaves or large sage leaves

▲ 4 ears of corn, husks and silk removed and each cut crosswise in quarters

4 teaspoons light mayonnaise

¼ cup grated Parmesan cheese

¼ teaspoon smoked paprika

To make it a meal

Serve steamed baby spinach sprinkled with lemon juice, which is both health-ful and flavorful.

1 Mix together yogurt, mustard, lemon juice, garlic, salt, and pepper in large zip-close plastic bag; add chicken. Squeeze out air and seal bag; turn to coat chicken. Refrigerate, turning bag occasionally, at least 1 hour or up to overnight.

2 Meanwhile, soak 4 (12-inch) and 8 (6-inch) wooden skewers in water 30 minutes. Preheat grill to medium or prepare medium-hot fire.

3 Remove chicken from marinade; discard marinade. Alter-nately thread chicken, lemon, and bay leaves onto 12-inch skewers. Spray with olive oil nonstick spray. Thread corn onto 6-inch skewers, dividing evenly.

4 Place chicken and corn on grill rack. Grill, turning occasionally, until chicken is cooked through and corn is just tender, about 12 minutes. Transfer to platter. Brush corn with mayonnaise; sprinkle evenly with Parmesan and paprika.

 Per serving (1 chicken kebab and 2 corn kebabs)

**Grilled Chicken and
Corn Kebabs**

Shrimp Risotto with Snap Peas SERVES 6

2 teaspoons olive oil
▲ 1 small fennel bulb, thinly sliced
1 shallot, thinly sliced
1 garlic clove, minced
¼ cup dry white wine
1 cup Arborio rice
▲ 3 cups reduced-sodium chicken broth
▲ ¾ pound medium shrimp, peeled and deveined
▲ ½ cup sugar snap peas, trimmed
Grated zest of 1 lemon
½ teaspoon salt

To make it a meal

Baby peas lend just the right touch of spring flavor to this delicately flavored risotto. Stir ¾ cup of thawed frozen baby peas into the risotto along with the snap peas for no additional *PointsPlus* value.

1 Heat oil in 6- to 8-cup rice cooker until hot, about 5 minutes. Add fennel, shallot, and garlic; cook, stirring, until vegetables are tender, about 5 minutes. Add wine and cook, stirring occasionally, until liquid is almost evaporated, 3–4 minutes.

2 Stir rice and broth into cooker; cover and cook until liquid is almost absorbed and rice is just tender, 20–25 minutes. Stir in shrimp, peas, zest, and salt; cook, covered, until shrimp is just opaque and peas are tender, about 3 minutes.

 Per serving (generous ¾ cup)

Vegetarian Skillet Bolognese SERVES 4

▲ 2 cups whole wheat penne

1 tablespoon plus 1 teaspoon extra-virgin olive oil

2 large shallots, finely chopped

▲ 2 carrots, shredded

2 large garlic cloves, minced

▲ 1 ⅓ cups refrigerated or frozen meatless soy crumbles

▲ 2 (14 ½-ounce) cans no-salt-added stewed tomatoes

1 tablespoon plus 1 teaspoon red-wine vinegar

½ teaspoon salt

½ teaspoon Italian seasoning or dried oregano

¼ teaspoon black pepper

To make it a meal

Begin with an arugula, orange, and fennel salad dressed with lemon juice.

1 Cook pasta according to package directions, omitting salt if desired. Drain and keep warm.

2 Meanwhile, to make sauce, heat oil in large nonstick skillet over medium heat. Add shallots and cook, stirring, until golden, about 2 minutes. Add carrot and garlic; cook stirring, until carrots are crisp-tender, about 1 minute. Add soy crumbles, tomatoes, vinegar, Italian seasoning, salt, and pepper; bring to boil. Reduce heat and simmer until sauce is heated through and flavors are blended, about 10 minutes. Serve over pasta.

 Per serving (1 cup sauce with 1 cup pasta)

pac
a

k snack

veggies, fruits, nuts, and more

Mini Antipasto

Cheesy Celery   SERVES 1

Fill **1 large celery stalk** with **2 tablespoons low-calorie garlic-and-herb cheese spread**.

 Per serving (1 filled celery stalk)

Red Ants on a Log   SERVES 1

Spread **1 teaspoon smooth peanut butter** on each of **3 celery stalks**. Top each with **4 dried cranberries**.

 Per serving (3 filled celery stalks)

Mini Antipasto   SERVES 1

Wrap **1 (½-ounce) slice prosciutto** around **1 stick part-skim string cheese**. Serve with **3 black or green brine-cured olives**.

 Per serving (1 cheese stick with 3 small olives)

Quick Microwave-Baked Apple SERVES 1

Fill **1 cored small apple** with **2 teaspoons packed brown sugar**, **2 tablespoons dark raisins**, **pinch ground cinnamon**, and **pinch ground nutmeg**. Microwave on High until apple is just tender, 3–4 minutes.

 Per serving (1 stuffed apple)

Tofu-Berry Smoothie SERVES 1

Combine **3 ounces silken tofu**, **½ cup frozen unsweetened blueberries**, **½ banana**, and **¾ cup fat-free milk** in blender; blend until smooth.

 Per serving (1 drink)

Spicy Hummus   SERVES 1

Mix together **¼ cup hummus**, **1 teaspoon chopped sun-dried tomato (not oil-packed)**, **pinch ground cumin**, and **pinch ground ginger** in small bowl. Serve with **½ cup sliced cucumber**.

 Per serving (¼ cup hummus and ½ cup cucumber)

Hummus-Avocado "Pizza"   SERVES 1

Spread **1 small whole wheat pita bread** with **2 tablespoons hummus**; top with **⅛ sliced Hass avocado**.

 Per serving (1 topped pita bread)

Cheesy Popcorn   SERVES 1

Toss together **3 cups plain air-popped popcorn**, **2 tablespoons grated Parmesan cheese**, **¼ teaspoon salt**, and **¼ teaspoon black pepper** in medium bowl.

 Per serving (3 cups popcorn)

Pimiento Toasts   SERVES 1

Mix together **2 tablespoons whipped cream cheese**, **1 tablespoon shredded fat-free Cheddar cheese**, **1 tablespoon drained and chopped roasted pepper (not oil-packed)**, and **pinch cayenne** in small bowl. Spread evenly on **4 slices melba toast**.

 Per serving (4 topped toasts)

Devil's Almonds   SERVES 1

Stir together **23 blanched whole almonds**, **pinch cayenne pepper**, and **pinch paprika** in small bowl.

 Per serving (23 almonds)

Apricot Bites   SERVES 1

Sprinkle **6 dried apricot halves** with **1 tablespoon crumbled blue cheese** and **1 teaspoon finely chopped unsalted pistachios**.

 Per serving (6 topped apricots)

Pimiento Toasts

Crunchy Banana Pops SERVES 1

Cut **1 banana in half** and insert popsicle stick into cut end of each half. Roll banana in **½ cup crushed honey-nut cereal**.

 Per serving (2 banana halves)

Apple-Nut Crisp SERVES 1

Spread **1 tablespoon reduced-fat smooth peanut butter** on **½ whole wheat matzo**. Top with **¼ thinly sliced apple** and **½ teaspoon honey**.

 Per serving (1 crisp)

Coconut-Berry Shake SERVES 1

Combine **1 cup halved strawberries, ½ sliced small banana, ⅓ cup ice cubes, ¼ cup light (reduced-fat) coconut milk, 1 tablespoon confectioners' sugar**, and **juice of 1 lime** in blender; blend until smooth.

 Per serving (1 drink)

Banana–Peanut Butter Freeze SERVES 1

Combine **1 sliced frozen banana, 1 tablespoon fat-free milk, 1 ½ teaspoons peanut butter**, and **¼ teaspoon ground cinnamon** in food processor or blender; process until creamy. Spoon into dessert dish.

 Per serving (about 1 cup)

Kale "Crisps" SERVES 1

Preheat oven to 350°F. Toss together **3 cups loosely packed torn kale leaves** with **1 teaspoon olive oil**, **pinch salt**, and **pinch black pepper** in medium bowl. Spread in single layer on baking sheet. Bake until crispy, about 10 minutes.

 Per serving (3 cups kale crisps)

Roasted Spiced Chickpeas SERVES 1

Preheat oven to 400°F. Stir together **½ cup canned chickpeas, rinsed and drained**, with **½ teaspoon extra-virgin olive oil**, **¼ teaspoon ground cumin**, **pinch salt**, and **pinch cayenne** in small bowl. Spread in single layer in small shallow baking pan. Bake until crunchy, about 25 minutes.

 Per serving (½ cup)

Guacamole SERVES 1

Coarsely mash **¼ pitted and peeled Hass avocado** in small bowl. Stir in **2 tablespoons seeded and chopped cucumber**, **1 tablespoon chopped red bell pepper**, **2 teaspoons lime juice**, **pinch chili powder**, and **pinch salt**.

 Per serving (½ cup)

Popcorn–Honey Peanut Mix SERVES 1

Mix together **1 ½ teaspoons light butter**, melted, **⅛ teaspoon green jalapeño pepper sauce**, and **pinch chili powder** in medium bowl. Add **1 ½ cups plain air-popped popcorn** and **1 tablespoon chopped honey-roasted peanuts**; toss until mixed well.

 Per serving (1 ½ cups)

Guacamole

cook it
in more time

Fall Fruit Crunch Mix SERVES 16

▲ 2 large egg whites
¼ cup sugar
1 teaspoon ground cinnamon
1 teaspoon paprika
¾ teaspoon salt
½ teaspoon ground cumin
¼–½ teaspoon cayenne
4 cups crispy corn squares cereal
3 cups multigrain O's cereal
2 cups multigrain pretzel nuggets with sesame seeds
(6 ounces)
½ cup chopped pecans
⅓ cup pumpkin seeds
½ cup coarsely chopped dried apples
½ cup dried cranberries

1 Preheat oven 300°F. Line large rimmed baking sheet with parchment paper.

2 Whisk together egg whites, sugar, cinnamon, paprika, salt, cumin, and cayenne in large bowl until blended well. Add corn squares cereal, O's cereal, pretzels, pecans, and pumpkin seeds; toss until coated evenly.

3 Spread mixture in single layer in pan. Bake, stirring every 10 minutes, until cereal is lightly browned and dry, about 30 minutes. Let cool in pan on wire rack. Transfer mixture to large bowl; stir in dried apples and cranberries. Can be stored in airtight container up to 1 week.

 Per serving (about ⅔ cup)

Caramel-Cashew Popcorn   SERVES 8

▲ 6 cups plain air-popped popcorn (about ¼ cup kernels)
 ¼ cup coarsely chopped salted roasted cashews
 ½ cup sugar
 ⅓ cup light corn syrup
 1 tablespoon unsalted butter, softened
 ½ teaspoon salt
 ⅛ teaspoon baking soda

1 Preheat oven to 325°F. Spray large heavy baking sheet with nonstick spray.

2 Spread popcorn and cashews in single layer on baking sheet.

3 Combine sugar, corn syrup, butter, and salt in small heavy saucepan and set over medium-low heat. Cook, stirring constantly, until sugar is dissolved. Increase heat to medium-high and bring to boil; boil until temperature on candy thermometer registers 250°F (hard-ball stage).

4 Remove pan from heat and stir in baking soda. Pour sugar mixture over popcorn and cashews and toss with pancake spatula until coated evenly. (Be careful; mixture will be very hot.)

5 Bake popcorn mixture 10 minutes; stir and turn with pancake spatula to ensure all popcorn is coated. Bake, stirring twice, until golden brown, about 10 minutes longer. Stir again and let cool completely on baking sheet on wire rack. Break up any clumps of popcorn. Popcorn can be stored in airtight container at room temperature up to 1 week.

 Per serving (⅔ cup)

e

njoy
dessert

cookies, pies, and cakes

Chocolate-Drizzled
Macaroons

Chocolate-Drizzled Macaroons   SERVES 1

Place **2 small coconut macaroon cookies** on wax paper—
lined plate. Drizzle **¼ ounce bittersweet or semisweet
chocolate**, melted in microwave, over cookies. Refrigerate
until chocolate is set, about 15 minutes.

 Per serving (2 cookies)

Lemon-Ginger Cookie Stacks   SERVES 1

Stir together **3 tablespoons plain fat-free Greek yogurt**,
3 tablespoons thawed frozen light whipped topping,
¼ teaspoon grated lemon zest, and **1 teaspoon lemon
juice** in small bowl. Top **2 thin ginger cookies** evenly with
half of lemon mixture; top each with **3 fresh raspberries**.
Repeat layering with 2 more cookies and remaining lemon
mixture; top each stack with **2 fresh raspberries**.

 Per serving (2 cookie stacks)

**Pumpkin-Orange
"Ice-Cream" Pie**

Mixed Berries with Balsamic and Orange Ricotta SERVES 4

Bring **½ cup balsamic vinegar** to boil in medium saucepan; boil until reduced to ¼ cup, about 4 minutes. Remove from heat; let cool about 5 minutes. Put **1 cup fat-free ricotta cheese** in mini or regular food processor and process until smooth and creamy. Scrape into small bowl. Mix together **2 (6-ounce) containers fresh raspberries**, **1 (6-ounce) container fresh blueberries**, and **1 (6-ounce) container fresh blackberries** in medium bowl. Divide evenly among 4 dessert dishes or wineglasses; drizzle with balsamic syrup. Top evenly with ricotta; sprinkle with **2 teaspoons grated orange zest**.

 Per serving (1 dessert)

To make it a meal

Serve this light and flavorful dessert after the hearty and richly flavored Grilled Braciole with Tomatoes on page 122.

Pumpkin-Orange "Ice-Cream" Pie

SERVES 12

Stir together ⅓ cup canned pumpkin puree, **2 tablespoons packed brown sugar**, and **1 teaspoon pumpkin pie spice** in large bowl until sugar is dissolved. Fold in **1 ½ cups slightly softened vanilla low-fat frozen yogurt** until blended. Spread over bottom of **1 (6-ounce) chocolate pie crust**. Freeze until firm, about 1 hour. Spread **1 ½ cups slightly softened orange sherbet** over pumpkin layer. Freeze until firm, about 1 hour. Spread **1 ½ cups slightly softened vanilla low-fat frozen yogurt** over sherbet to cover. Wrap pie tightly in plastic wrap and freeze overnight or up to 2 weeks. To serve, soften pie slightly in refrigerator, about 15 minutes. Spread **1 ½ cups thawed frozen light whipped topping** over filling; garnish with fresh orange wedges.

 Per serving (1/12 of pie)

Vanilla Custards with Apricot Jam SERVES 6

Preheat oven to 350°F. Spray 6 (6-ounce) custard cups with nonstick spray. Combine **1 ½ cups low-fat (1%) milk**, **½ cup instant nonfat dry milk**, and **¼ cup sugar** in medium saucepan and set over medium-high heat. Cook, stirring, until bubbles form around edge and sugar is dissolved, 4–5 minutes. Remove saucepan from heat. Beat **3 large eggs** in small bowl. Whisk about ½ cup of milk mixture into beaten eggs to temper them. Whisk in **1 teaspoon vanilla extract**. Whisk egg mixture back into saucepan. Pour custard mixture through sieve into custard cups. Put custards in roasting pan and place in oven. Pour enough hot (not boiling) water into pan to come halfway up sides of cups. Bake until tip of knife inserted into center of custard comes out clean, 20–25 minutes. Transfer custards to wire rack and let cool to room temperature. Refrigerate until cold, at least 4 hours or up to overnight. Serve custards topped with **6 tablespoons apricot or cloudberry jam**.

 Per serving (1 custard with 1 tablespoon jam)

To make it a meal

The French Lamb Stew with Eggplant and Tomatoes on page 139 is the perfect menu companion for these exceptional custards.

Honeydew with Fresh Raspberry Sauce

SERVES 4

From **2 (6-ounce) containers fresh raspberries**, pick out and reserve 12 berries for garnish. Combine remaining berries and **1 teaspoon lemon juice** in blender; blend until smooth. Pour puree through sieve set over small bowl, pressing hard to extract as much liquid as possible. Discard seeds. Cut **1 small honeydew or Crenshaw melon** lengthwise in half; scoop out and discard seeds. Cut each half into 8 wedges; cut off rind. Spoon about ¼ cup raspberry sauce on each of 4 plates. Arrange 4 melon wedges on each plate. Top melon with reserved berries and **fresh mint sprigs**.

 Per serving (1 plate)

Vanilla Custards with Apricot Jam

**Rosemary and Olive Oil
Chiffon Cake**

Rosemary and Olive Oil Chiffon Cake

SERVES 16

1 ½ cups cake flour

1 ½ teaspoons baking powder

½ teaspoon salt

1 ¼ cups granulated sugar

1 ½ tablespoons finely chopped fresh rosemary

▲ 7 large eggs, separated and at room temperature

⅔ cup tepid water

½ teaspoon vanilla extract

¼ cup fruity extra-virgin olive oil

¼ teaspoon cream of tartar

1 ½ tablespoons confectioners' sugar

To make it a meal

This special rosemary-scented cake is a great way to follow the satisfying Sirloin Steak with Watercress Salad on page 121.

1 Place oven rack in lower third of oven and preheat oven to 325°F. Line bottom of ungreased 10-inch tube pan with parchment paper.

2 Whisk together flour, baking powder, and salt in medium bowl. Whisk together 1 cup of granulated sugar and the rosemary in large bowl until fragrant. Add egg yolks and whisk until lightened. Whisk in water and vanilla until blended. Slowly add oil in thin, steady stream, whisking, until mixed well. Fold in flour mixture until blended.

3 With electric mixer on medium speed, beat egg whites and cream of tartar until soft peaks form when beaters are lifted. Increase speed to high. Add remaining ¼ cup granulated sugar, 1 tablespoon at a time, beating until stiff peaks form. Fold beaten whites into yolk mixture, just until blended.

4 Scrape batter into tube pan; spread evenly. Bake until cake is golden brown and springs back when lightly pressed, about 55 minutes, rotating pan from front to back halfway through baking time. Invert pan onto its legs or neck of bottle and let cool completely. Run thin knife around edge of cake to loosen it from side and center tube of pan. Remove cake from pan; dust with confectioners' sugar.

 Per serving (¹⁄₁₆ of cake)

Pineapple Tres
Leches Cake

Pineapple Tres Leches Cake   SERVES 16

2 cups cake flour

¾ cup granulated sugar

2 teaspoons baking powder

½ teaspoon salt

1 (8-ounce) can crushed pineapple

▲ 4 large eggs, separated and at room temperature

⅓ cup canola oil

▲ 2 large egg whites, at room temperature

½ teaspoon cream of tartar

1 cup fat-free evaporated milk

1 cup fat-free sweetened condensed milk

▲ ½ cup fat-free milk

½ cup unsweetened coconut shavings, toasted

1 Preheat oven to 350°F. Spray 9 x 13-inch baking pan with nonstick spray.

2 Whisk flour, ½ cup of sugar, the baking powder, and salt in medium bowl. Drain pineapple, reserving 3 tablespoons juice. Combine pineapple and reserved juice, 4 egg yolks, and oil in large bowl; stir until mixed well. Stir in flour mixture.

3 With electric mixer on medium speed, beat 6 egg whites and cream of tartar in large bowl until soft peaks form when beaters are lifted. Increase speed to high. Add remaining ¼ cup sugar, 1 tablespoon at a time, beating until stiff, glossy peaks form. With rubber spatula, stir about one fourth of beaten egg whites into flour mixture to lighten. Gently fold in remaining whites.

4 Scrape batter into pan; spread evenly. Bake until cake is golden brown and springs back when lightly pressed, about 45 minutes. Place cake in pan on wire rack and let cool.

5 Stir together evaporated milk, sweetened condensed milk, and fat-free milk in medium bowl. With wooden skewer, poke holes all over top of cooled cake. Spoon milk mixture evenly over top. Let cake stand until milk mixture is absorbed, about 15 minutes. Sprinkle with toasted coconut. Cover cake with plastic wrap and refrigerate at least 4 hours or up to overnight.

 Per serving (¹⁄₁₆ of cake)

Chocolate-Spice Cupcakes   MAKES 12

2 cups all-purpose flour

1 ½ teaspoons baking soda

1 teaspoon five-spice powder

1 teaspoon ground ginger

¼ teaspoon salt

½ cup semisweet chocolate chips

¾ cup light (mild) molasses

▲ ½ cup fat-free egg substitute

¼ cup canola oil

½ cup hot water

2 tablespoons turbinado (raw sugar)

1 Preheat oven to 350°F. Spray 12 muffin pan cups with nonstick spray or line with paper liners.

2 To make batter, whisk together flour, baking soda, five-spice powder, ginger, and salt in large bowl; stir in chocolate chips. Whisk together molasses, egg substitute, and oil in medium bowl. Add molasses mixture to flour mixture; stir just until mixed well. Stir in hot water until blended.

3 Divide batter evenly among muffin cups; sprinkle with turbinado. Bake until toothpick inserted into center of cupcake comes out clean, 20–22 minutes. Let cool in pan on wire rack 5 minutes. Remove cupcakes from pan and let cool completely on rack.

 Per serving (1 cupcake)

Chocolate-Spice Cupcakes

Raspberry Cheesecake Pie   SERVES 12

1 refrigerated pie crust (from 14.1-ounce package)

1 cup part-skim ricotta cheese

▲ 6 tablespoons fat-free egg substitute

¼ cup sugar

1 teaspoon grated lemon zest

¼ teaspoon almond extract

▲ 2 cups fresh raspberries

1 tablespoon currant jelly, melted

1 tablespoon chopped unsalted pistachios

1 Preheat oven to 400°F.

2 Soften pie crust according to package directions. Ease crust into 9-inch pie plate, pressing it against side of plate. Crimp edge to form decorative rim. Line crust with sheet of nonstick foil; fill with dried beans or raw rice.

3 Bake until edge of crust is set, about 10 minutes; remove foil with beans. Bake until center of crust is dry and set, about 10 minutes longer. Let cool completely on wire rack.

4 Reduce oven temperature to 350°F.

5 To make filling, puree ricotta cheese in food processor. Add egg substitute, sugar, lemon zest, and almond extract; pulse just until blended. Spoon filling into crust and spread evenly. Bake until filling is set, 35–40 minutes. Let cool completely on rack. Can be covered and refrigerated up to 1 day.

6 To serve, arrange raspberries over filling. Brush berries with melted jelly; sprinkle with pistachios.

 Per serving (¹/₁₂ of pie)

Shortbread Cookies MAKES 40

3 tablespoons cold unsalted butter, cut into pieces

¼ cup confectioners' sugar

▲ 1 large egg white, lightly beaten

½ cup all-purpose flour

1 (3-inch) piece vanilla bean, split and scraped

1 ½ teaspoons granulated sugar

To make it a meal

Crumbly, buttery shortbread cookies are the perfect casual dessert treat after enjoying our Oven-Fried Chicken with Buttermilk Gravy on page 124.

1 Combine butter and confectioners' sugar in food processor; pulse 10–12 times, or until mixture forms fine crumbs. Add 1 tablespoon of egg white; pulse just until blended. Cover and refrigerate remaining egg white. Add flour and vanilla seeds; pulse just until mixture comes together (it will be crumbly).

2 Transfer dough to lightly floured work surface. Form into ball, then roll into 10-inch log. Wrap log in plastic wrap; refrigerate until firm, at least 2 hours or up to overnight.

3 Preheat oven to 350°F. Line large baking sheet with parchment paper.

4 Spread granulated sugar on sheet of wax paper. Brush dough log with 2 teaspoons reserved egg white; roll in granulated sugar. Cut log into ¼-inch slices. Place cookies 1 inch apart on baking sheet. Bake until cookies are firm in center and edges are golden, 10–12 minutes. Transfer cookies with parchment to wire rack; let cool completely. Cookies can be stored in airtight container up to 1 week.

 Per serving (4 cookies)

Cranberry-Pear Shortcakes   SERVES 8

▲ 1 ½ cups fresh or frozen cranberries

▲ 2 pears, peeled, cored, and finely chopped

  ¾ cup water

  ⅓ cup sugar

  2 cups white whole wheat flour

  2 teaspoons baking powder

  ½ teaspoon baking soda

  ½ teaspoon salt

  3 tablespoons light stick butter, cut into pieces and chilled

▲ ¾ cup plain fat-free yogurt

  3 (6-ounce) containers lemon fat-free yogurt

1 To make filling, combine cranberries, pears, water, and sugar in medium saucepan. Bring to boil over medium-high heat, stirring frequently. Reduce heat and simmer, stirring, until mixture is thickened and syrupy, about 5 minutes. Remove pan from heat.

2 Meanwhile, preheat oven to 400°F.

3 To make shortcakes, whisk together flour, baking powder, baking soda, and salt in medium bowl. With pastry blender or two knives used scissors-style, cut in butter until mixture is crumbly. Add plain yogurt in two batches, stirring with fork just until blended. Knead dough 6 times in bowl. Transfer dough to lightly floured surface and pat to ½-inch thickness.

4 Using floured 2 ½-inch round cutter, cut dough into rounds, rerolling scraps, making total of 8 biscuits. Place biscuits 1 inch apart on ungreased baking sheet. Bake until golden brown, about 15 minutes.

5 Split warm biscuits; place bottoms of biscuits on 8 plates. Top each with ½ cup cranberry filling and cover with tops of biscuits. Serve with lemon yogurt.

 Per serving (1 shortcake with 3 tablespoons yogurt)

Cranberry-Pear
Shortcakes

mix
a

drink

alcoholic and non-alcoholic

Mulled Wine SERVES 6 • ALCOHOLIC

Combine **1 (750-ml) bottle dry red wine**, **1 (3-inch) cinnamon stick**, **1 teaspoon cracked black peppercorns**, **2 tablespoons brandy**, **1 tablespoon sugar**, **2 (3-inch) strips orange zest**, and **½ teaspoon fennel seeds, crushed**, in large saucepan. Bring just to boil; reduce heat and simmer 10 minutes. Remove pan from heat; let cool completely. Pour wine mixture through sieve set over large bowl; discard solids. Pour mulled wine into 6 glasses. Garnish with **6 cinnamon sticks** and **3 dried apricots, halved**.

 4 Per serving (½ cup)

White Rum Caipirinhas SERVES 6 • ALCOHOLIC

With muddler or handle of wooden spoon, mash **2 quartered limes** with **2 ½ tablespoons packed brown sugar** in pitcher. Stir in **4 (12-ounce) cans zero-calorie all-natural lemon-lime soda**, **2 cups ice cubes**, **5 ounces white rum**, and **½ cup lime juice (about 4 limes)**. Fill 6 glasses with **ice cubes**; pour rum mixture over ice.

3 Per serving (about 1 cup)

To make it a meal

Serve this tropical drink as the perfect accompaniment to the Orange Pork on page 119.

Orange and White Wine Spritzers

SERVES 8 • ALCOHOLIC

Half-fill pitcher with **ice cubes**. Add **1 (750-ml) bottle chilled dry white wine**, **2 (12-ounce) cans plain seltzer**, and **6 tablespoons orange-flavored liqueur**. Pour into 8 glasses. Garnish with **8 thin slices orange**, **3 tablespoons pomegranate seeds**, and **8 fresh mint sprigs**.

 Per serving (⅔ cup without ice)

Cherry-Pear Bubbly   SERVES 6 • ALCOHOLIC

Divide **6 tablespoons chilled pear nectar** and **6 maraschino cherries** among 6 glasses. Top evenly with **1 (750-ml) bottle chilled sparkling wine**. Garnish with **6 rosemary sprigs**.

 Per serving (½ cup)

**Cranberry-Citrus Sparklers,
Strawberry Lemonade,
Honeydew-Grape Smoothies**

Cranberry-Citrus Sparklers

SERVES 8 • NON-ALCOHOLIC

Put **4 cups ice cubes**, **1 ½ cups water**, **1 (12-ounce) can frozen orange-cranberry juice concentrate**, and **½ cup lime juice (about 4 limes)** in blender; blend until ice is chopped. Pour into pitcher and stir in **2 (12-ounce) cans sugar-free lemon-flavored sparkling water**.

 Per serving (1 cup)

Strawberry Lemonade   SERVES 8 • NON-ALCOHOLIC

Mash **1 (1-pound) container fresh strawberries, hulled**, with **3 tablespoons sugar** in medium bowl until small pieces of strawberries remain and mixture is juicy. Let stand 5 minutes. Pour into pitcher; add **6 ½ cups water**, **1 (12-ounce) can thawed frozen lemonade concentrate**, and **2 cups ice cubes**. Stir until blended well.

 Per serving (1 ½ cups)

Honeydew-Grape Smoothies

SERVES 4 • NON-ALCOHOLIC

Combine **2 cups peeled and cubed honeydew melon**, **2 cups green seedless grapes**, and **⅔ cup chilled white grape juice** in blender and puree. With machine running, slowly add **½ cup ice cubes** through feed tube; blend until thick and smooth.

 Per serving (¾ cup)

Melon Agua Fresca   SERVES 6 • NON-ALCOHOLIC

Halve, seed, and cube **2 cantaloupes (about 8 cups)**. Puree 4 cups of melon with **½ cup cold water** in blender. Pour into pitcher. Repeat with remaining melon and **½ cup cold water**. Add **3 tablespoons superfine sugar** and **juice of 2 limes**; stir until sugar is dissolved. Fill 6 glasses with **ice cubes**. Pour fruit mixture over ice. Garnish with **thin slices lime**.

 Per serving (1 cup without ice)

To make it a meal
Enjoy agua fresca, a popular drink in Mexico especially during the hot weather. Try it with the Tex-Mex Chicken Tacos on page 58.

Vanilla-Pomegranate Smoothie
SERVES 1 • NON-ALCOHOLIC

Combine **1 (6-ounce) container vanilla fat-free yogurt**, **½ peeled and diced small apple**, **⅓ cup pomegranate juice**, and **¼ cup crushed ice** in blender: blend until smooth.

 Per serving (1 ½ cups)

To make it a meal
This smoothie is a refreshing and satisfying drink for relatively few *PointsPlus* value. Serve it for dessert after having the Chicken and Cheese on page 27 for lunch.

Soy-Berry Energy Shake
SERVES 1 • NON-ALCOHOLIC

Puree **¾ cup vanilla soy milk**, **½ banana**, **¼ cup frozen unsweetened mixed berries**, and **1 tablespoon flaxseed meal** in blender; blend until smooth.

 Per serving (1 ⅓ cups)

Melon Agua Fresca

make it
in a little time

Mint Iced Tea   SERVES 6 • NON-ALCOHOLIC

Pour **3 cups very hot but not boiling water** over **6 green tea bags** and **½ cup mint leaves** in teapot; cover and brew 2 ½–3 minutes. Pour through sieve into heatproof pitcher; discard tea and mint. Stir in **1 tablespoon honey**; add **3 cups cold water**. Fill 6 glasses with **ice cubes**; pour tea over ice.

 Per serving (1 cup tea without ice)

To make it a meal
The Saigon Sub on page 31 is a great match for this refreshing iced tea drink. For dessert have some juicy ripe strawberries sprinkled with finely grated orange zest.

Mint and Melon-Ade   SERVES 1 • NON-ALCOHOLIC

Squeeze juice from **1 quartered lemon** into pitcher. Add squeezed lemon quarters. Add **½ cup loosely packed fresh mint leaves** and **¼ cup sugar**; mash with muddler or handle of wooden spoon until sugar is dissolved. Puree **5 cups diced seedless watermelon** in blender. Pour through sieve into pitcher; stir. Fill glass with **ice cubes**; pour melon-ade over ice.

 Per serving (1 ¼ cups without ice)

Tropical Cranberry Spritzers

SERVES 6 • NON-ALCOHOLIC

Stir together **1 ½ cups cran-strawberry juice** and **1 ½ cups guava-passion fruit juice** in pitcher. Cover pitcher with plastic wrap; refrigerate until well chilled, at least 3 hours or up to 1 day. To serve, stir **3 cups seltzer** into pitcher; fill with **ice cubes**. Pour spritzer mixture into 6 glasses. Cut **1 lime** into 6 wedges. Squeeze **1 lime wedge** into each drink; add wedges to drinks.

 Per serving (1 cup without ice)

Pom-Berry Fizz   SERVES 1 • NON-ALCOHOLIC

Combine **2 cups pomegranate juice** and **3 slices unpeeled fresh ginger** in small saucepan; bring just to boil. Reduce heat and simmer 10 minutes. Pour pomegranate juice mixture into medium metal bowl; let come to room temperature. Place in freezer until very cold, at least 3 hours; discard ginger. Pour juice into pitcher; stir in **4 cups unsweetened cherry-flavored seltzer** and **½ cup fresh blueberries**. Fill glass with **ice cubes**. Pour drink over ice.

 Per serving (1 ⅔ cups without ice)

Mango-Ginger Float

Chocolate-Cherry Cooler

SERVES 1 • NON-ALCOHOLIC

Combine **1 cup almond milk**, **10 frozen unsweetened sweet cherries**, and **1 packet fat-free cocoa mix** in blender; blend until smooth.

 Per serving (about 1 ⅓ cups)

Mango-Ginger Float   SERVES 1 • NON-ALCOHOLIC

Combine **¼ peeled and pitted mango, chopped**, and **juice of ½ small lime** in mini-food processor; process until smooth. Pour into glass. Top with **½-cup scoop mango sorbet** and **⅔ cup diet ginger ale**.

 Per serving (about 1 ¼ cups)

Kicked-Up Cocoa   SERVES 1 • NON-ALCOHOLIC

Heat **1 cup fat-free milk** in small saucepan set over low heat until bubbles appear around edge. Stir in **1 packet no-sugar-added cocoa** and **¼ teaspoon cayenne**.

 Per serving (1 cup)

take
your

time

weekend cooking

Orange Pork

Orange Pork   SERVES 6

Zest of 1 orange, removed in strips with vegetable peeler

½ cup water

¼ cup dry white wine

3 whole black peppercorns

½ bay leaf

¼ plus ⅛ teaspoon salt

▲ 1 (1 ½-pound) lean pork tenderloin, trimmed

1 tablespoon fresh thyme leaves

2 tablespoons packed brown sugar

2 teaspoons extra-virgin olive oil

To make it a meal

Serve the pork with a radicchio and endive salad along with a bowl of brown rice and beans. Three cups of cooked brown rice mixed with a 15 ½-ounce can of rinsed and drained black beans, warmed, will up the per-serving *PointsPlus* value by **4**).

1 To make caramelized orange, combine orange zest, water, wine, peppercorns, bay leaf, and ⅛ teaspoon of salt in small saucepan; bring to boil. Reduce heat and simmer until orange strips are tender, about 25 minutes. Let cool in liquid. Drain. Transfer strips to cup.

2 Preheat oven to 375°F.

3 Sprinkle pork with remaining ¼ teaspoon salt. Cut orange zest into 1-inch pieces. Place pieces of zest over top of pork; spray zest with olive oil nonstick spray; sprinkle with thyme and brown sugar, pressing to adhere. Drizzle pork with oil.

4 Heat large cast-iron skillet over medium-high heat until drop of water sizzles in pan, about 3 minutes. Add pork, topping side down, and cook until browned, about 4 minutes. Carefully turn pork and cook, turning every 2 minutes, until browned on all sides, about 5 minutes. Transfer to oven. Roast until instant-read thermometer inserted into center of pork registers 145°F for medium, about 20 minutes. Transfer pork to cutting board; let stand 5 minutes. Cut into 18 slices. Serve pork drizzled with pan drippings.

 Per serving (3 slices pork with 1 ½ teaspoons pan drippings)

Smoky Flank Steak with Chimichurri

SERVES 6

3 tablespoons red-wine vinegar

1 tablespoon extra-virgin olive oil

3 tablespoons chopped fresh cilantro

3 tablespoons chopped fresh flat-leaf parsley

1 garlic clove, minced

¾ teaspoon salt

½ teaspoon dried oregano

1 teaspoon chipotle chile powder

Pinch red pepper flakes

▲ 1 (1 ¼-pound) lean flank steak, trimmed

To make it a meal

Put out a bowl of farro sprinkled with parsley and grilled or broiled tomato halves seasoned with dried oregano (½ cup cooked farro per serving will increase the *PointsPlus* value by *3*).

1 Spray grill rack with nonstick spray. Preheat grill to medium or prepare medium-hot fire.

2 Meanwhile, to make chimichurri, combine vinegar, oil, cilantro, parsley, garlic, ¼ teaspoon of salt, and the oregano in small bowl.

3 Mix together the chile powder, pepper flakes, and remaining ½ teaspoon salt in cup. Rub over both sides of steak.

4 Place steak on the grill rack and grill until instant-read thermometer inserted into center of steak registers 145°F for medium, about 5 minutes per side. Transfer steak to cutting board and let stand about 5 minutes. Cut steak across grain on angle into 18 slices. Serve with chimichurri.

 Per serving (3 slices steak with 4 teaspoons chimichurri)

Sirloin Steak with Watercress Salad

SERVES 4

Juice of ½ lemon

2 teaspoons olive oil

1 teaspoon Dijon mustard

½ teaspoon Worcestershire sauce

4 large shallots, thinly sliced

▲ 1 (1-pound) lean beef strip sirloin steak, trimmed

¼ teaspoon salt

¼ teaspoon black pepper

▲ 1 (4-ounce) bag watercress, trimmed

▲ ¼ cup crumbled fat-free feta cheese

To make it a meal

A bowl of steamed baby potatoes sprinkled with parsley is an ideal side for this special steak dish (5 ounces of steamed baby potatoes for each serving will increase the **PointsPlus** value by **3**).

1 To make dressing, whisk together lemon juice, oil, mustard, and Worcestershire sauce in large bowl.

2 Spray large nonstick skillet with nonstick spray and set over medium heat. Add shallots and cook, stirring, until softened, about 4 minutes. Transfer to dressing in bowl.

3 Sprinkle steak with salt and pepper. Add steak to skillet and cook until instant-read thermometer inserted into center of steak registers 145°F for medium, about 4 minutes per side. Transfer steak to cutting board and let stand 3 minutes.

4 Meanwhile, to make salad, add watercress and feta cheese to dressing; toss until mixed well.

5 Thinly slice steak across grain into 12 slices; serve with salad.

 Per serving (3 slices steak with 1 ¼ cups salad)

Grilled Braciole with Tomatoes SERVES 4

- ▲ 12 sun-dried tomatoes (not oil-packed)
- ▲ ¼ cup finely chopped scallions
-   3 tablespoons Italian-seasoned panko (Japanese bread crumbs)
-   2 tablespoons grated Pecorino Romano cheese
-   4 teaspoons olive oil
-   1 teaspoon dried oregano
- ▲ 1 (1-pound) lean center-cut beef tenderloin, trimmed
- ▲ 1 (12-ounce) container mixed baby tomatoes, quartered
-   1 tablespoon balsamic vinegar
-   ¼ teaspoon salt
-   ¼ teaspoon black pepper
- ▲ 4 small portobello mushrooms, stemmed
-   ½ cup thinly sliced fresh basil

To make it a meal

Start with a classic Italian salad of very thinly sliced raw baby artichokes, fennel, and mushrooms dressed with lemon juice and black pepper. Then end with a small bowl of seedless grapes and strawberries.

1 Soak 8 (6-inch) wooden skewers in water 30 minutes.

2 To make stuffing, combine sun-dried tomatoes with boiling water to cover in small bowl; let stand 20 minutes. Drain and chop. Mix together sun-dried tomatoes, scallions, panko, Romano, 2 teaspoons of oil, and the oregano in small bowl.

3 With knife held parallel to board and against long side of beef, cut three-quarters of way through beef and open up like a book. Place piece of plastic wrap on beef and pound to ¾-inch thickness. Spread stuffing over beef, pressing lightly. Starting at one long side, tightly roll up, jelly-roll fashion. Tie with string at 1½-inch intervals. Cut roll between ties to make 4 braciole; secure each with 2 skewers.

4 To make tomato salad, stir together baby tomatoes, vinegar, remaining 2 teaspoons oil, the salt, and pepper.

5 Preheat grill to medium-high or prepare medium-hot fire. Spray braciole and mushrooms with nonstick spray. Place on grill rack. Grill mushrooms until tender, about 3 minutes per side. Grill braciole 6 minutes per side for medium; remove skewers and string. Stir basil and mushroom juices into tomato salad.

 Per serving (1 braciole with 1 mushroom and ½ cup tomato salad)

Pork Cutlets with Bourbon Cream Sauce SERVES 4

2 tablespoons plus 3 teaspoons all-purpose flour

½ teaspoon dried thyme

¼ teaspoon salt

¼ teaspoon black pepper

▲ 4 (¼-pound) lean center-cut loin pork cutlets (¼ inch thick), trimmed

2 teaspoons olive oil

¼ cup bourbon

▲ ⅔ cup reduced-sodium chicken broth

1 teaspoon packed brown sugar

▲ ¼ cup fat-free half-and-half

To make it a meal

Steamed green beans and cooked brown rice served alongside the pork make for a satisfying meal (½ cup cooked brown rice per serving will increase the *PointsPlus* value by *3*).

1 Mix together 2 tablespoons plus 2 teaspoons of flour, the thyme, salt, and pepper on sheet of wax paper. Coat cutlets, one at a time, with flour mixture, shaking off any excess.

2 Heat 1 teaspoon of oil in large nonstick skillet over medium heat. Add 2 cutlets and cook until lightly browned, 1–2 minutes per side. Transfer to plate and keep warm. Repeat with remaining 1 teaspoon oil and cutlets.

3 Add bourbon to skillet and cook, stirring constantly, until mixture starts to reduce, about 20 seconds. Stir in broth and brown sugar; bring to boil. Reduce heat to low and simmer until mixture starts to thicken, 1–2 minutes. Whisk together half-and-half and remaining 1 teaspoon flour in cup until smooth; stir into bourbon mixture. Cook, stirring constantly, until sauce bubbles and thickens, about 1 minute longer. Serve over pork.

 Per serving (1 pork cutlet with generous 1 tablespoon sauce)

Oven-Fried Chicken with Buttermilk Gravy SERVES 6

1 cup plus 2 tablespoons low-fat buttermilk

▲ 1 large egg white

½ teaspoon salt

½ teaspoon black pepper

6 (5-ounce) bone-in chicken thighs or drumsticks, skinned

⅔ cup whole wheat panko (Japanese bread crumbs)

1 tablespoon plus 2 teaspoons all-purpose flour

¼ teaspoon cayenne

2 teaspoons canola oil

▲ 1 small onion, finely chopped

▲ ¾ cup reduced-sodium chicken broth

To make it a meal

Serving a bowl of steamed zucchini alongside the chicken is tasty and good for you. This green is rich in vitamins B, C, K, and E.

1 With fork, beat 1 cup of buttermilk, the egg white, salt, and pepper in pie plate or shallow dish. Add chicken, turning to coat. Cover and refrigerate, turning occasionally, at least 1 hour or up to overnight.

2 Preheat oven to 400°F. Spray large rimmed baking sheet with nonstick spray.

3 Mix together panko, 1 tablespoon of flour, and the cayenne on sheet of wax paper. Coat chicken, one piece at a time, with panko mixture, pressing so it adheres. Place chicken in single layer on baking sheet; lightly spray with nonstick spray. Bake, without turning, until golden brown and cooked through, about 40 minutes.

4 To make gravy, heat oil in small saucepan over medium heat. Add onion and cook, stirring occasionally, until softened, about 5 minutes. Stir in remaining 2 teaspoons flour until blended. Whisk in broth until smooth; bring to boil. Reduce heat and simmer, whisking constantly, until sauce bubbles and thickens, about 1 minute. Remove pan from heat; whisk in remaining 2 tablespoons buttermilk. Serve with chicken.

 Per serving (1 piece chicken with ¼ cup gravy)

Oven-Fried Chicken
with Buttermilk Gravy

Spring Lamb Stew with Baby Vegetables SERVES 6

3 teaspoons olive oil

▲ 1 ½ pounds lean boneless leg of lamb, trimmed and cut into 1-inch chunks

▲ 2 cups baby carrots, trimmed or baby-cut carrots

▲ 1 cup frozen small white onions

4 large garlic cloves, minced

▲ 1 (14 ½-ounce) can reduced-sodium beef broth

▲ 1 pound small (about 1-inch) potatoes, scrubbed

1 tablespoon plus 2 teaspoons chopped fresh thyme

¾ teaspoon salt

¼ teaspoon black pepper

▲ 1 cup frozen baby peas

2 tablespoons chopped fresh parsley

2 teaspoons chopped fresh rosemary

1 Heat 2 teaspoons of oil in nonstick Dutch oven over medium heat. Add half of lamb and cook, turning, until browned on all sides, about 6 minutes. Transfer lamb to plate. Repeat with remaining lamb.

2 Add remaining 1 teaspoon oil to Dutch oven. Add carrots and onions; cook, stirring, until vegetables are lightly browned, about 4 minutes. Stir in garlic and cook, stirring, until fragrant, about 1 minute longer. Stir in broth, potatoes, lamb, 2 teaspoons of thyme, the salt, and pepper; bring to boil. Reduce heat and simmer, covered, until lamb is tender and vegetables are softened, about 50 minutes. About 10 minutes before cooking time is up, stir in peas.

3 Mix together parsley, rosemary, and remaining 1 tablespoon thyme. Sprinkle over each serving of stew.

 Per serving (about 1 ½ cups)

Middle Eastern-Style Chicken with Cucumber-Yogurt Sauce SERVES 4

- ▲ 1 pound chicken tenders
- 2 tablespoons white-wine vinegar
- 2 large garlic cloves, minced
- 1 teaspoon dried oregano
- ¾ teaspoon salt
- ¼ plus ⅛ teaspoon black pepper
- ▲ ¾ cup plain fat-free yogurt
- ▲ ¾ cup finely diced English (seedless) cucumber
- 4 tablespoons chopped fresh mint
- 2 tablespoons chopped fresh dill
- ½ teaspoon ground cumin
- 2 teaspoons olive oil
- ▲ 2 cups thinly sliced romaine lettuce
- ▲ 1 large tomato, diced
- ▲ ½ cup thinly sliced red onion

To make it a meal

This light and flavorful main dish only needs a dessert to turn it into a complete meal. Frozen green grapes are refreshing and no work at all.

1 Combine chicken, vinegar, garlic, oregano, ½ teaspoon of salt, and ¼ teaspoon of pepper in large bowl; stir until mixed well. Let stand 10 minutes or refrigerate up to 2 hours.

2 Meanwhile, to make yogurt sauce, stir together yogurt, cucumber, 2 tablespoons of mint, the dill, cumin, remaining ¼ teaspoon salt and ⅛ teaspoon pepper in small bowl.

3 Heat oil in large nonstick skillet over medium heat. Add chicken and cook until browned and cooked through, about 2 minutes per side. Transfer chicken to plate and let cool slightly.

4 Divide lettuce evenly among 4 plates; top evenly with chicken, tomato, onion, and yogurt sauce. Sprinkle with remaining 2 tablespoons mint.

Per serving (about 3 chicken tenders with ¼ of salad and about ⅓ cup sauce)

Skillet Chicken and Peppers with Tomato Salsa SERVES 4

- ▲ 1 pint cherry tomatoes, quartered
- ¼ cup chopped fresh cilantro
- ▲ 1 small scallion, thinly sliced
- 1 tablespoon lime juice
- ▲ 4 (5-ounce) skinless boneless chicken breasts, thinly sliced crosswise
- ½ teaspoon salt
- ¼ teaspoon black pepper
- 2 teaspoons extra-virgin olive oil
- ▲ 1 small red onion, sliced
- ▲ 1 red bell pepper, thinly sliced
- ▲ 1 yellow bell pepper, thinly sliced
- 1 teaspoon dried oregano
- Pinch cayenne

To make it a meal

Cook up a pot of whole wheat spaghetti to serve with our best-ever chicken and peppers dish (1 cup of cooked whole wheat spaghetti per serving will increase the *PointsPlus* value by **4**).

1 To make salsa, mix together tomatoes, cilantro, scallion, and lime juice in small serving bowl.

2 Sprinkle chicken with salt and black pepper. Heat oil in large nonstick skillet over medium heat. Add half of chicken and cook, stirring, until golden and cooked through, about 5 minutes. Transfer chicken to plate. Repeat with remaining chicken.

3 Spray skillet with nonstick spray. Add onion and bell peppers; cook, stirring, until vegetables are softened, about 6 minutes. Add chicken, oregano, and cayenne; cook, stirring frequently, until chicken is heated through, about 1 minute. Serve with salsa.

 Per serving (1 cup chicken mixture with ⅓ cup salsa)

Mexican-Style Halibut   SERVES 4

- ▲ 1 cup matchstick-cut carrots
- ▲ 1 small red bell pepper, cut into matchstick strips
- ▲ 1 small red onion, thinly sliced
- ▲ 4 (5-ounce) halibut fillets
- ¾ teaspoon salt
- ¼ teaspoon black pepper
- ▲ 1 cup drained diced fire-roasted tomatoes
- ▲ ½ cup thawed frozen corn kernels
- ▲ 1 jalapeño pepper, seeded and minced
- 4 teaspoons extra-virgin olive oil
- ¼ cup chopped fresh cilantro
- 4 lime wedges

To make it a meal

Prepare a batch of brown rice and mix it with finely chopped parsley, dill, chives, and basil (½ cup cooked brown rice per serving will increase the *PointsPlus* value by *3*). For dessert serve thick slices seedless watermelon sprinkled with fresh lime juice.

1 Preheat oven to 425°F. Tear off 4 (16-inch) sheets of foil; spray centers with nonstick spray.

2 Bring 1 inch of water to boil in medium saucepan. Add carrots, bell pepper, and onion. Reduce heat and simmer, covered, until vegetables are slightly wilted but still crunchy, about 1 minute; drain.

3 Place 1 halibut fillet in center of each piece of foil; sprinkle with ½ teaspoon of salt and ⅛ teaspoon of black pepper. Top each piece of fish with one fourth of vegetable mixture, tomatoes, corn, and jalapeño. Drizzle evenly with oil.

4 To close packets, bring two opposite long sides of foil up to meet in center. Fold edges over twice, making ½-inch-wide folds to seal tightly. Double-fold two remaining open sides to seal tightly. Transfer packets to large rimmed baking sheet.

5 Bake until fish is just opaque in center, about 12 minutes. To check for doneness, open one packet (be careful of steam). If fish is not fully cooked, reseal packet and bake until cooked through. Serve sprinkled with cilantro and with lime wedges.

 Per serving (1 halibut fillet with ¼ of vegetables)

Ultimate Mac 'n' Cheese

Ultimate Mac 'n' Cheese   SERVES 8

▲ 1 cup cubed butternut squash

▲ 3 cups whole wheat elbow macaroni

⅓ cup panko (Japanese bread crumbs)

5 tablespoons grated Pecorino Romano cheese

1 teaspoon olive oil

▲ 2 ¼ cups fat-free milk

3 tablespoons all-purpose flour

2 ounces light cream cheese (Neufchâtel), softened

1 teaspoon salt

½ teaspoon Dijon mustard

1 small garlic clove, minced

⅛ teaspoon cayenne

1 ½ cups shredded low-fat sharp Cheddar cheese

1 Combine butternut squash and enough cold water to cover by 1 inch in small saucepan. Bring to boil. Reduce heat and simmer, covered, until squash is tender, about 15 minutes. Drain. Transfer squash to mini food processor and puree.

2 Cook elbow macaroni according to package directions, omitting salt if desired. Drain.

3 Meanwhile, to make topping, mix together panko, 3 tablespoons of Romano, and oil in small bowl.

4 Preheat broiler. Spray 2 ½-quart shallow flameproof baking dish with nonstick spray.

5 Whisk together milk and flour in dry pasta pot until smooth; add cream cheese. Cook over medium heat, whisking constantly, until mixture is smooth and comes to boil. Whisk in salt, mustard, garlic, and cayenne. Reduce heat and simmer, whisking frequently, until mixture is thickened, about 2 minutes. Remove from heat. Add Cheddar, remaining 2 tablespoons Romano, and squash, stirring until cheeses are melted. Stir in macaroni.

6 Spoon macaroni mixture into baking dish; sprinkle with topping. Broil until top is lightly browned.

 Per serving (1 cup)

To make it a meal

Start on a light note by serving a salad of baby spinach, arugula, baby romaine, grape tomatoes, and thinly sliced radishes dressed with your favorite fat-free dressing. Topping it with croutons made from 4 slices of toasted reduced-calorie whole wheat bread will increase the per-serving **PointsPlus** value by **1**.

Thai Mussel Pot   SERVES 6

- 4 ounces rice stick noodles
- 2 teaspoons canola oil
- ▲ 1 or 2 jalapeño peppers, seeded and thinly sliced
- 2 shallots, thinly sliced
- 1 tablespoon minced peeled fresh ginger
- 2 garlic cloves, minced
- ▲ 8 ounces shiitake mushrooms, stemmed and sliced
- ▲ 3 cups vegetable broth
- ½ cup dry white wine
- 1 tablespoon Asian fish sauce
- ▲ 3 pounds mussels, scrubbed
- ⅓ cup chopped fresh basil
- Grated zest of 1 lime

To make it a meal

End with a tasty mix of halved strawberries, diced fresh pineapple, and canned unsweetened mandarin orange segments.

1 Place noodles in large bowl. Add enough hot water to cover; let stand until noodles are softened, about 10 minutes. Drain.

2 Meanwhile, heat oil in large nonstick saucepan over medium heat. Add jalapeño, shallots, ginger, and garlic; cook, stirring frequently, until fragrant, about 1 minute. Add mushrooms and cook, stirring, until softened, about 2 minutes. Stir in broth, wine, and fish sauce; bring to boil. Add mussels and cook, covered, until mussels open, about 4 minutes. Discard any mussels that do not open.

3 To serve, divide noodles evenly among 6 bowls. With slotted spoon, divide mussels among bowls; ladle broth over. Mix together basil and lime zest in small bowl; sprinkle over stew.

 Per serving (⅓ cup noodles with about 12 mussels and ⅔ cup broth)

Risotto-Style Vegetables and Tofu

SERVES 4

- ▲ 3 cups vegetable broth
- 4 teaspoons olive oil
- ▲ ¾ pound reduced-fat firm tofu, cubed
- ▲ ½ pound shiitake mushrooms, stemmed and thickly sliced
- ¼ teaspoon salt
- ¼ teaspoon black pepper
- ▲ ½ pound asparagus, trimmed and cut into 1-inch pieces
- ▲ 1 small onion, finely chopped
- ▲ ¾ cup quick-cooking brown rice
- Grated zest and juice of ½ lemon
- ▲ 1 cup frozen peas

To make it a meal

Begin with a salad of packaged cooked beets sprinkled with fat-free feta cheese and mint, and end with juicy slices of fresh pineapple— look for it already cored— sprinkled with chopped fresh cilantro (1 ounce of crumbled fat-free feta cheese per serving will increase the **PointsPlus** value by **1**).

1 Bring broth to simmer in medium saucepan over medium heat. Reduce heat to low and maintain low simmer.

2 Meanwhile, heat 2 teaspoons of oil in large nonstick skillet over medium heat. Add tofu and cook, stirring occasionally, until golden, about 6 minutes. Transfer to plate.

3 Add 1 teaspoon oil to skillet. Add mushrooms, salt, and pepper; cook, stirring, until mushrooms have released their liquid, about 5 minutes. Add asparagus and cook until crisp-tender, about 3 minutes. Transfer to plate.

4 Add remaining 1 teaspoon oil and the onion to skillet. Cook, stirring, until softened, about 5 minutes. Add rice and lemon juice; cook, stirring, until liquid is evaporated. Add ½ cup of hot broth and cook, stirring constantly, until broth is almost completely absorbed, about 1 minute. Add remaining 2 ½ cups broth and bring to boil. Reduce heat and simmer, covered, until rice is almost tender, about 30 minutes (there should be quite a bit of liquid remaining).

5 Uncover skillet; increase heat and bring to boil. Cook until liquid is almost completely absorbed. Add tofu mixture and peas; cook, stirring, until heated through, about 1 minute. Remove from heat. Let stand 5 minutes. Divide rice mixture among 4 bowls. Sprinkle with lemon zest.

 **Per serving (1 ½ cups)**

Creamy Greek Veggie Bake SERVES 6

2 teaspoons olive oil

▲ 1 (8-ounce) package sliced cremini mushrooms

▲ 1 red bell pepper, chopped

▲ 1 onion, chopped

▲ 1 (12-ounce) bag frozen meatless soy crumbles

▲ 1 (14 ½-ounce) can fire-roasted petite diced tomatoes

▲ ½ cup vegetable broth

1 teaspoon ground cinnamon

¼ teaspoon salt

▲ 1 large eggplant, cut into ½-inch rounds

3 tablespoons all-purpose flour

▲ 1 ¾ cups fat-free milk

▲ 1 large egg

⅓ cup grated Parmesan cheese

To make it a meal

Steamed baby spinach sprinkled with fresh lemon juice is a great side for this special meatless casserole.

1 To make filling, heat oil in large nonstick skillet over medium heat. Add mushrooms, bell pepper, and onion; cook, stirring, until softened, about 8 minutes. Add soy crumbles and cook, stirring, until browned, about 5 minutes. Stir in tomatoes, broth, cinnamon, and salt; bring to boil. Reduce heat and simmer, covered, stirring occasionally, until slightly thickened, about 15 minutes. Remove skillet from heat.

2 Spray broiler rack with nonstick spray; preheat broiler. Spray 9 x 13-inch baking dish with nonstick spray.

3 Place eggplant on broiler rack; spray with nonstick spray. Broil until lightly browned, about 5 minutes per side.

4 Preheat oven to 375°F.

5 To make sauce, whisk flour and milk in small saucepan. Cook over medium heat, whisking constantly, until mixture bubbles and thickens. Remove pan from heat. Beat egg in small bowl; gradually whisk in ½ cup of hot milk mixture. Add egg mixture to saucepan. Stir in Parmesan.

6 Arrange half of eggplant in baking dish; cover with filling. Top with remaining eggplant and sauce. Bake until heated through, about 30 minutes. Cool 15 minutes before serving.

 Per serving (1 cup)

Creamy Greek Veggie Bake

Savory Stuffed Artichokes SERVES 4

▲ 4 (14-ounce) artichokes

1 lemon, halved

1 cup dried whole wheat bread crumbs

⅓ cup plus 2 tablespoons grated Pecorino Romano cheese

▲ 1 large plum tomato, finely chopped

¼ cup chopped fresh flat-leaf parsley

4 garlic cloves, finely chopped

1 tablespoon extra-virgin olive oil

⅛ teaspoon salt

4 lemon wedges

To make it a meal

Broiled or grilled large or extra-large shrimp are a flavorful match for our tempting stuffed artichokes (3 ounces of cooked shrimp per serving will increase the **PointsPlus** value by **2**).

1 Preheat oven to 425°F.

2 To trim artichokes, bend back outer green leaves from base and snap off. With kitchen scissors, trim thorny tops of leaves; rub all cut surfaces with cut half of lemon to prevent browning. Cut off stem. Cut 1 inch off top of artichoke. Spread open artichoke leaves to expose fuzzy choke. With melon baller or tip of teaspoon, scoop out choke and discard. Squeeze remaining lemon half into large bowl of water. Put artichoke in lemon water. Repeat with remaining artichokes.

3 To make stuffing, mix together bread crumbs, ⅓ cup of Romano, the tomato, parsley, garlic, oil, and salt in medium bowl. Drain artichokes; fill centers evenly with stuffing, spoon remaining stuffing between leaves.

4 Place artichokes in 2-quart shallow baking dish. Pour enough boiling water into dish to come halfway up sides of dish. Cover dish tightly with heavy-duty foil. Bake 50 minutes. Uncover and sprinkle artichokes with remaining 2 tablespoons Romano. Bake until artichoke bottoms are tender when pierced with tip of knife, about 10 minutes longer. Serve with lemon wedges.

 Per serving (1 stuffed artichoke)

Savory Stuffed
Artichokes

Beef-Mushroom Stew with Tomatoes and Garlic   SERVES 6

▲ 1 pound lean boneless beef bottom round, trimmed and cut into 1-inch chunks

▲ 3 leeks (white and light green parts only), halved lengthwise and sliced

1 teaspoon dried thyme

1 teaspoon dried rosemary

¾ teaspoon salt

¼ teaspoon black pepper

4 large garlic cloves, minced

▲ 1 (28-ounce) can diced tomatoes

1 cup dry red wine

1 bay leaf

1 teaspoon extra-virgin olive oil

▲ 4 small portobello mushrooms (about 1 pound), stemmed and sliced

½ cup mixed olives (not oil-packed), pitted

3 tablespoons chopped fresh flat-leaf parsley

Grated zest of 1 orange

To make it a meal

Lightly crush cooked all-purpose potatoes with a potato masher and serve with this Mediterranean-style stew. Be sure to spoon some of the flavorful juices on top (1 ½ pounds of cooked all-purpose potatoes will increase the per-serving *PointsPlus* value by *3*).

1 Combine beef, leeks, thyme, rosemary, ½ teaspoon of salt, and all but 1 teaspoon of garlic in 5- or 6-quart slow cooker. Transfer remaining garlic to dish; cover and refrigerate. Stir in tomatoes, wine, and bay leaf. Cover and cook until beef is fork-tender, 4–5 hours on high or 8–10 hours on low.

2 About 20 minutes before cooking time is up, heat oil in large nonstick skillet over medium heat. Add mushrooms, reserved garlic, and remaining ¼ teaspoon salt; cook until mushrooms brown and any liquid is evaporated, about 5 minutes. Add mushrooms and olives to slow cooker. Cover and cook on high until mushrooms are tender, about 10 minutes longer.

3 Mix together parsley and orange zest in small bowl. Sprinkle over stew.

 **Per serving (1 cup)**

French Lamb Stew with Eggplant and Tomatoes SERVES 4

1 pound lean boneless lamb shoulder, trimmed and cut into 1-inch chunks

½ teaspoon salt

¼ teaspoon black pepper

▲ 1 (14 ½-ounce) can reduced-sodium beef broth

▲ 1 (14 ½-ounce) can diced tomatoes

▲ 1 (1-pound) eggplant, cubed

▲ 1 onion, chopped

3 large garlic cloves, minced

1 tablespoon chopped fresh rosemary

▲ 1 large yellow bell pepper, cut into 1-inch pieces

▲ 1 large zucchini, cut into 1-inch chunks

2 tablespoons prepared pesto

To make it a meal

Spoon this flavor-packed stew over whole wheat orzo, then enjoy a bowl of fresh seasonal fruit for dessert (½ cup cooked whole wheat orzo per serving will increase the *PointsPlus* value by **2**).

1 Sprinkle lamb with salt and pepper. Heat large nonstick skillet over medium heat. Add lamb and cook, turning occasionally, until browned, about 6 minutes. Transfer lamb to 5- or 6-quart slow cooker.

2 Add broth to skillet and bring to boil, scraping any browned bits from bottom of pan. Pour broth over lamb. Add tomatoes with juice, eggplant, onion, garlic, and rosemary; mix well. Cover and cook until lamb and vegetables are fork-tender, 4–5 hours on high or 8–10 hours on low.

3 About 40 minutes before cooking time is up, add bell pepper and zucchini to slow cooker. Cover and cook on high until vegetables are tender, about 35 minutes. Serve topped with pesto.

 Per serving (1 ¾ cups stew with ½ tablespoon pesto)

Chunky Hoisin Pork and Vegetables

SERVES 6

- ▲ 1 ½ pounds lean boneless center-cut pork loin, trimmed and cut into 1 ½-inch chunks
- 2 tablespoons minced peeled fresh ginger
- 4 large garlic cloves, minced
- ¾ teaspoon five-spice powder
- Pinch cayenne
- ▲ 2 ½ cups reduced-sodium vegetable broth
- ¼ cup hoisin sauce
- 2 tablespoons reduced-sodium soy sauce
- 1 tablespoon cornstarch
- ▲ 1 (16-ounce) bag frozen broccoli stir-fry mix
- ▲ ½ pound mixed mushrooms, thickly sliced (if using shiitakes, remove stems)

To make it a meal

A bowl of steamed white or brown rice is just the right vehicle for absorbing all the flavorful juices in this richly flavored main dish (½ cup cooked white or brown rice per serving will increase the **PointsPlus** value by **3**).

1 Combine pork, ginger, garlic, five-spice powder, and cayenne in 5- or 6-quart slow cooker. Add broth and hoisin sauce; stir until mixed well. Cover and cook until pork is fork-tender, 4–5 hours on high or 8–10 hours on low.

2 With slotted spoon, transfer pork to medium bowl. Whisk together soy sauce and cornstarch in cup until smooth. Gradually stir cornstarch mixture into slow cooker. Cover and cook on high until sauce simmers, about 10 minutes. Stir in broccoli mix and mushrooms. Cover and cook on high until vegetables are tender, about 40 minutes. Gently stir in pork and cook until heated through, about 10 minutes longer.

 Per serving (about 1 cup)

**Chunky Hoisin Pork
and Vegetables**

Cannellini Bean, Fennel, and Sausage Stew SERVES 6

- ▲ 1 onion, chopped
- ▲ 2 (15 ½-ounce) cans cannellini (white kidney) beans, rinsed and drained
- ▲ 1 large fennel bulb, quartered and sliced
- ▲ 1 large red bell pepper, sliced
- 4 large garlic cloves, minced
- 1 pound sweet Italian turkey sausage, cut into 1 ½-inch chunks
- ▲ 1 (14 ½-ounce) can stewed tomatoes
- ▲ ½ cup reduced-sodium chicken broth
- 3 tablespoons chopped fresh basil
- 2 tablespoons chopped fresh flat-leaf parsley
- ¼ cup grated Parmesan cheese

To make it a meal

To make it a meal, serve steamed wax or green beans and halved and toasted light rolls alongside this robust Italian favorite (1 light roll per serving will increase the **PointsPlus** value by **2**).

Layer onion, beans, fennel, bell pepper, garlic, sausage, and tomatoes in 5- or 6-quart slow cooker. Add broth. Cover and cook until sausage and vegetables are fork-tender, 4–5 hours on high or 8–10 hours on low. Stir in parsley. Serve sprinkled with Parmesan.

 Per serving (1 ⅓ cups)

Provençal Vegetable Soup with Pistou

SERVES 4

4 teaspoons extra-virgin olive oil

▲ 3 leeks (white and light green parts only), sliced

3 large garlic cloves, peeled

½ teaspoon fennel seeds

▲ 1 small fennel bulb, diced

▲ 2 small baking potatoes, peeled and chopped

▲ 1 (14 ½-ounce) can peeled whole tomatoes, broken up

4 (3-inch) strips orange zest

1 teaspoon herbes de Provence

½ teaspoon salt

¼ teaspoon black pepper

▲ 2 (32-ounce) containers reduced-sodium chicken broth

1 cup loosely packed fresh basil leaves

2 tablespoons grated Parmesan cheese

To make it a meal

Start with grilled herbed mushroom caps, and end with wedges of cantaloupe topped with whole strawberries.

1 Heat 2 teaspoons of oil in large nonstick skillet over medium heat. Add leeks and garlic; cook, stirring, until leeks are softened, about 5 minutes. Add fennel seeds and cook, stirring constantly, until fragrant, about 1 minute.

2 Transfer leek mixture to 5- or 6-quart slow cooker. Add chopped fennel, potatoes, tomatoes, orange zest, herbes de Provence, salt, and pepper. Add broth. Cover and cook until vegetables are fork-tender, 4–5 hours on high or 8–10 hours on low.

3 Meanwhile, to make pistou, combine basil, Parmesan, and remaining 2 teaspoons oil in mini food processor; pulse until smooth.

4 Discard garlic and orange zest from soup. Ladle soup into 4 bowls. Top with pistou.

 Per serving (2 ½ cups soup with 1 tablespoon pistou)

Chicken in White Wine

Chicken in White Wine   SERVES 8

½ teaspoon canola oil

4 slices turkey bacon, cut into ½-inch pieces

▲ 1 large onion, chopped

▲ 1 (1-pound) bag baby-cut carrots

8 (5-ounce) chicken thighs or drumsticks, skinned

½ teaspoon salt

¼ teaspoon black pepper

1 cup dry white wine

▲ ¾ cup reduced-sodium chicken broth

1 ½ teaspoons herbes de Provence

¼ cup chopped fresh flat-leaf parsley

To make it a meal

Enjoy this dish with steamed haricots verts (slender green beans) and 1 ¾ pounds of cooked baby potatoes sprinkled with your choice of fresh herbs. This will increase the per-serving **PointsPlus** value by **2**.

1 Coat large nonstick skillet with oil and set over medium heat. Add bacon and cook, stirring frequently, until lightly browned, about 3 minutes. Add onion and cook, stirring, until softened and golden, about 8 minutes. Transfer bacon mixture to 5- or 6-quart slow cooker; add carrots.

2 Sprinkle chicken with salt and pepper; spray with nonstick spray. Add to skillet and set over medium heat. Add half of chicken and cook until browned, about 5 minutes per side. Transfer chicken to slow cooker. Repeat with remaining chicken.

3 Add wine to skillet and bring to boil, scraping any browned bits from bottom of skillet. Add wine mixture, broth, and herbes de Provence to slow cooker; stir until mixed well. Cover and cook until chicken and vegetables are fork-tender, 3–4 hours on high or 6–8 hours on low. Serve sprinkled with parsley.

 Per serving (1 piece chicken with about ¾ cup vegetables and sauce)

Manhattan-Style Clam Chowder   SERVES 6

2 teaspoons extra-virgin olive oil

▲ 2 onions, chopped

▲ 2 (14 ½-ounce) cans fire-roasted diced tomatoes

▲ 2 (10-ounce) cans baby clams

▲ 2 baking potatoes, peeled and diced

3 fresh flat-leaf parsley sprigs plus ½ cup finely chopped flat-leaf parsley

½ teaspoon dried oregano

¼ teaspoon salt

¼ teaspoon red pepper flakes or to taste

¼ teaspoon black pepper

7 cups water

To make it a meal

As a first course, serve a mixed green salad topped with shredded fat-free Cheddar cheese (1 ounce of shredded fat-free Cheddar cheese per serving will increase the **PointsPlus** value by **1**).

1 Heat oil in large nonstick skillet over medium heat. Add onions and cook, stirring, until softened, about 5 minutes.

2 Transfer onions to 5- or 6-quart slow cooker. Add tomatoes, clams with their juice, potatoes, parsley sprigs, oregano, salt, pepper flakes, and black pepper. Add water. Cover and cook until vegetables are fork-tender, 4–5 hours on high or 8–10 hours on low. Discard parsley sprigs. Ladle soup into 6 bowls. Sprinkle with chopped parsley.

 Per serving (2 cups)

**Manhattan-Style
Clam Chowder**

Spiced Dried Cherry-Pear Bread Pudding SERVES 10

1 (½-pound) piece day-old crusty bread, cubed (about 5 cups)

▲ 2 large pears, peeled and coarsely chopped (about 3 cups)

½ cup dried cherries or cranberries

2 cups low-fat (1%) milk

▲ 1 cup fat-free half-and-half

½ cup packed brown sugar

▲ 2 large eggs

▲ 1 large egg white

1 tablespoon brandy

2 teaspoons vanilla extract

1 teaspoon pumpkin pie spice

1 tablespoon confectioners' sugar

1 Spray 5- or 6-quart slow cooker with removable stoneware insert with nonstick spray. Mix together bread, pears, and cherries in slow cooker. Whisk together milk, half-and-half, brown sugar, eggs, egg white, brandy, vanilla, and pumpkin pie spice in large bowl; pour over bread mixture.

2 Cover slow cooker tightly with foil, then place lid on top. Cook until toothpick inserted into center of pudding comes out clean, about 3 hours on high or 5 hours on low.

3 Transfer pudding with stoneware insert to wire rack; let cool 15 minutes. Run thin knife around edge of pudding to loosen it from stoneware. Invert onto large serving plate. Dust with confectioners' sugar. Serve warm or at room temperature.

 Per serving (about ½ cup)

Orange and Cinnamon-Scented Rice Pudding SERVES 6

4 tablespoons flaked sweetened coconut

6 tablespoons sugar

2 cups low-fat (1%) milk

▲ 1 cup fat-free half-and-half

½ cup Arborio rice

1 teaspoon grated orange zest

⅛ teaspoon ground cinnamon

1 ½ teaspoons vanilla extract

To make it a meal

Enjoy this delectable slow-cooker dessert as the perfect ending for our Skillet Chicken and Peppers with Tomato Salsa on page 128.

1 Chop 2 tablespoons of coconut; place in 4-quart slow cooker.

2 Combine sugar and ½ cup of milk in microwavable bowl or glass measure. Microwave on High until milk is steaming hot, about 1 minute; stir until sugar is dissolved. Pour milk mixture into slow cooker. Add remaining 1 ½ cups milk, the half-and-half, rice, orange zest, and cinnamon; stir until mixed well. Cover and cook until rice is tender, 3 hours on high or 6 hours on low.

3 Stir vanilla into pudding; sprinkle with remaining 2 tablespoons coconut. Serve warm or cold.

 Per serving (about ½ cup)

Recipes by *PointsPlus* value

Index